Sizzling
SEX

Other books by Dr Pam Spurr

Fabulous Foreplay – The Sex Doctor's Guide to Teasing and Pleasing Your Lover

Sensational Sex – The Revolutionary Guide to Sexual Pleasure and Fulfilment

Sex, Guys & Chocolate – Your Essential Guide to Erotic Pleasure

Sinful Sex – The Uninhibited Guide to Erotic Pleasure

The Dating Survival Guide – The Top Ten Tactics for Total Success

The Break-up Survival Kit – Emotional Rescue for the Newly Single

Dreams and Sexuality – Understanding Your Sexual Dreams

You & Him – Getting to the Heart of Your Relationship

Understanding Your Child's Dreams

Sizzling SEX

The Sex Doctor's 250 Hottest Tips, Tricks & Techniques

Dr Pam Spurr

JR
BOOKS

To Nick, you keep putting a smile on my face

First published in Great Britain in 2008 by
JR Books, 10 Greenland Street, London NW1 0ND
www.jrbooks.com

A catalogue record for this book is available from the British
Library.

ISBN 978-1-906217-65-5

1 3 5 7 9 10 8 6 4 2

Printed in the UK by CPI Bookmarque, Croydon, CR0 4TD

Contents

Acknowledgements   vii
Introduction: Let's Get the Party Started   1

Part One
Tips, Tricks and Techniques to Tempt Her With

Sextion One
Let Your Fingers Do the Walking – Sexy Touching Tips   9

Sextion Two
Tips for Delicious Oral Sex for Her Pleasure   25

Sextion Three
Tips to Liven Up Sex Positions for Her   38

Sextion Four
Tips for Enhancing Her Sexual Fantasies   51

Sextion Five
All Sorts of Tempting Tips for Her Pleasure   57

Part Two
Tips, Tricks and Techniques to Tempt Him With

Sextion One
Let Your Fingers Do the Walking – Sexy Touching Tips   67

Sextion Two
Tips for Delicious Oral Sex for His Pleasure   80

Sextion Three
Tips to Liven Up Sex Positions for Him   92

Sextion Four
Tips for Enhancing His Sexual Fantasies   103

Sextion Five
All Sorts of Sexy Tips for His Pleasure   110

Part Three
Tips, Tricks and Techniques for Both of You

Sextion One
Tips to Use with Rude Foods   119

Sextion Two
Playful Tips   128

Sextion Three
Downright Dirty and Very Rude Tips   141

Sextion Four
The 'Deluxe Dozen' Selection   154

Websites   162

Acknowledgements

A huge thank you to all the amazing, honest people who have shared intimate aspects of their sex lives with me. Without such help, it would have been a very difficult job to write this book.

A warm thank you also to Lesley Wilson, my editor, and Catherine Bailey, my publicist, both of whom are extremely easy to work with. Special thanks must go to Jeremy Robson who, as ever, is a pleasure to work with. Finally, I thank my children for their incredible patience when I work so hard on a book.

Safer Sex

This book is about sex tips, tricks, and techniques to bring you and your lover pleasure. It is your responsibility to ensure that your sexual health is protected. This means that if you are with a new partner, you should use safer-six techniques to help prevent transmission of sexual infections. There are many sources of information about safer-six techniques. And it is your responsibility to find out about these. Even if you are with a long-established partner, you must be careful with some of the sex tips, tricks and techniques I describe in order not to transmit infection, for example, through anal sex play.

Introduction

Let's Get the Party Started

This book is all about sexual pleasure and how you can enhance yours by using my favourite sex tips, tricks and techniques. Mind you, I'm not confessing to which ones I use personally! But every single technique in this book has come highly recommended, often from numerous, and separate, individuals.

So, why write a book that's all about tips, tricks and techniques and not include other areas, like, why people have bad sex? The reason for this is that having spoken to literally thousands of people over the years in my various roles, I found that those lovers who try out a new tip, trick or technique, even occasionally, are those with the most successful and exciting sex lives.

I'm going to let you into a secret: in the research for this book, I asked hundreds of people how often they tried a new sex technique once they were in an established relationship. Guess what? You may be shocked to hear that after the initial 'honeymoon period', and once a couple had been together for around a year, by far the majority of those questioned never tried a new technique. Not even one new tip, trick or technique. I find this quite staggering. Only around 10 per cent of couples introduced an occasional new technique to spice things up, and they are obviously in the rare minority. And if you've been in a relationship for more than two years, the picture is even bleaker – unless you're particularly experimental, you'll probably never again add any new sex technique into your love life.

It made me ask many of those I spoke to, 'Why on earth not?' The answers they gave were wide ranging, from people who were simply lazy in their sexual relationship to those who were worried that if they asked to try something new they'd hurt their partner's feelings. People were assuming that their partner would take it as a criticism if they wanted to try something different, rather than a celebration of sexual enjoyment.

The problem is, they're assuming the wrong thing!

As long as you suggest trying something new in a loving and even in a sensual way, no one is going to be offended.

Some people I spoke to about this issue felt they were in a sexual comfort zone and it was all quite pleasing and everything was 'fine'. But I have a warning for them – you may enjoy a sexual comfort zone for a few years but in time your lover may feel taken for granted, bored, and even become resentful. Sexual routines and ruts have helped to break up many relationships. Maybe they're not the only reason a couple parts but they can certainly add to any other existing troubles.

If you're like one of the 90 per cent of people I spoke to who haven't tried anything new for a long time, then this book is ideal for you. Throwing in even just an occasional tip, trick or technique can liven up and refresh your sexual relationship. This in turn can recharge your entire relationship because what your partner thinks in response to your little bit of initiative and sexual creativity is, 'Hey, this feels great. My partner really cares about my sexual pleasure, they find me sexy, and they want to keep things lively for both of us!'

As so many relationships break up because they fall into a rut, including a sexual rut, it's important that, as long as you both want to have sex, you at least occasionally try to make it new and exciting.

It only needs one tip, trick or technique to successfully do this and make a big difference to your relationship.

On the other hand, if you're in a new relationship, and still in that exciting phase where anything goes, this book is also ideal for you. It will give you many tips, tricks and techniques to try with your new lover and keep the magic alive, ranging from the sensuous to the eye watering. And, of course, if you're in a long-term relationship – and in the minority of 'sex-perimental' couples that occasionally throw in something new – then there's lots here to keep things as lively and sexy as you obviously expect them to be.

The Sex Doctor's Guide to Introducing New Tips, Tricks and Techniques into Your Sex Life

Here are 10 steps to help you introduce some fresh sex-play into your relationship without upsetting your partner or hurting their feelings.

• Always start by saying how much you enjoy the way your partner, for example, 'touches your breasts', and then add in what you'd like to try that's new. This way you make them feel positive about what they're already doing and more likely to want to try new things.

• You can let your fingers do part of the 'talking' and simply start touching your lover in a way that's suggestive of trying something new. You don't want to shock your lover by, say, suddenly whipping out some anal beads and asking them to pop them in! But you can gently start stroking their bottom and talking about anal pleasure.

Then see where the conversation leads.

• With many things you can let your fingers do all the 'talking' as you guide your lover's hands to new erogenous zones or, for example, during penetrative sex, slip the vibrator you two sometimes play with between you for extra pleasure during thrusting.

• Introduce a new tip, trick or technique as a little sex game. You can show your lover some dice you've got and suggest that you roll them with a view to having the numbers represent some new things to try.

• Try asking your lover when you're laying together, maybe just having a warm cuddle, what secret sexy things they think about trying. Reassure them that you want to hear what they think about and that will open up the chance for you to talk about your own secret ideas.

• Use birthdays, anniversaries and other special days as a time to say you've got something exciting you want to do to your lover. Frame it as if you're giving them their own special pleasure to celebrate the event.

• When talking about trying something new, never speak in a tone that suggests you're completely bored with the 'same old thing' you two have been doing for the past two years or however long you have been together.

• Never 'accuse' your lover of not wanting to try something new – even if it's true! Such accusations, valid or not, will definitely put a stop to them wanting to try something different with you.

• Show them this book while casually chatting and suggest you have fun by opening a page at random and agreeing that you'll try a sex tip from it.

• Enjoy an occasional 'refresher' weekend by suggesting you both get away from it all. Use that as the perfect time to try a new tip, trick or technique. Simply being in different surroundings makes people more likely to be a bit daring.

Now that you've got some tips to get you started trying sexy new things, let me explain how my book works. Part One is devoted to sex tips to use on the woman in your life. Part Two is completely dedicated to turning on the man in your life. And Part Three gives you a selection of tips from the fun to the downright dirty for both of you!

To make things easier for you, my tips aren't in any particular order. So when one leaps out at you as something you definitely want to try, you can do so at any appropriate time. You don't have to follow them from number 1 through to 250 in order, but instead you can enjoy some spontaneous fun. The simplicity of this book is that if you took any one of these tips and tossed it into your sex-play, say, every couple of weeks or so, you'd keep things interesting in and out of the bedroom for a very long time. That's not much to ask, particularly if you don't want to end up like the majority of couples who never try anything new after the first year of their relationship.

Part One

Tips, Tricks and Techniques to Tempt Her With

Sextion One

Let Your Fingers Do the Walking –
Sexy Touching Tips

Our skin is packed full of sensory nerve endings. Certain areas have more nerve endings than others, for instance your fingertips and the clitoris and penile glans have more sensitivity than your elbow. Also, in some areas where the skin is thinner, like inside of the wrist and behind the knee, the sense of touch is much more intense because the nerve endings are more exposed. Don't underestimate how much sexual enjoyment you can give your lover by using touch in different ways and in all of her erogenous zones.

Top Tips For Tender Touching

It's easy for men to forget just how sensitive a woman's skin is. You can merely brush against her breast and even through her sweater her nipples might spring to life because they are so sensitive to touch. Or, simply glancing your hand across the back of her head as you go to smooth her hair can send a little shiver of pleasure through her.

With such sensitivity, however, you need to optimise the part of your body that you are most likely to touch her with – your hands. Instead of being lazy about caring for your hands, do something about the rough skin of yours. You can begin by making sure your nails are trimmed. There's nothing worse than having a jagged nail edge catch your tender skin. Next, make sure any calluses on your hands are smoothed off with a nail buffer. You can also (secretly if you wish) regularly use hand cream to keep your hands moderately soft. There are plenty of male grooming products available for this kind of personal care.

When you come to touch your lover make sure your hands are warm by running them under some warm water before taking her to bed. Finally, keep asking her if the way you are touching her feels pleasurable. As her arousal intensifies she may want a more gentle or a firmer touch. Let the tips, tricks and techniques commence.

Intensify Her Feelings When Touched

As you are now looking after your most important tools for sensual touching (your hands), why not think about the ways you can help intensify your lover's pleasure? To give her a truly sensual experience and one that will maximise her sexual experience, you can help bring her skin to life. An easy but sexy tip, that she'll really appreciate, is for you to offer to exfoliate her skin.

You can either do this in the shower with a face cloth or during a massage with the express purpose of exfoliating her skin. In the shower, take some body scrub and squeeze some onto a clean face cloth. Ask her to stand there under a gentle, warm shower as you work the body scrub around her skin with circular motions. It feels fantastic and will heighten her pleasure when you touch her. Or, ask her to lie back on a warm towel while you gently use a body brush over her skin in long sweeping motions.

Exfoliating her skin will help reawaken all her nerve endings before foreplay.

Fabulous Feathering

This technique is one of the most erotic and pleasurable you can use on her. All you need is some massage oil, a feather, and her willingness to lie back. You can use this tip when you've been kissing and caressing and want to take things a bit further.

Have her lie back and gently remove her top – if it's not already off! Pour some massage oil on your hands and warm it up. Now, gently stroke the oil over her chest, breasts and tummy. Then, taking a clean feather – you can get one from an artists' supply shop or an adult shop – swirl the tip of it through the oil. You can swirl it back and forth across her chest and breasts, moving it through the oil. Then gently tease her nipples with the tip of it by circling them and ensuring there's plenty of lovely oil to smooth the way of the feather tip.

Work on down her body and ask her to part her legs. Using more massage oil to lubricate the inside of her thighs, next run the tip of the feather up and down, and around and around this entire erogenous zone.

This technique really heightens sensual pleasure because it builds anticipation that's not satisfied through the technique but will guarantee she's well on her way to sexual arousal.

What's Cooking?

One fantastic tip for becoming a great lover is to be creative with anything that comes to hand. Obviously you want to do this sensibly so don't use anything like, say, an empty champagne bottle, to pleasure your lover with. Something like a glass bottle can break off and severely injure your partner. Many lovers have got carried away after sharing a bottle of bubbly only to have it go terribly wrong and end up in A&E.

However, many things that you're likely to have around the home can make great spontaneous sex toys and you won't come to any harm with them. For example, the innocent kitchen basting brush can give you some fun and pleasure. Imagine that you two have shared a candlelit dinner. You're starting to flirt with each other and get in the mood. Why not unbutton your lover's blouse, take the bottle of olive oil, and smooth some across her breasts with the brush. Not only can such spontaneous fun lead to hot sex but it's also the sort of 'incident' you'll laugh about later on down the line: 'Remember that time you had me on the kitchen table after opening my top and rubbing cooking oil all over my breasts with the kitchen basting brush? You were such an animal!' And that's how easily memories are made!

Raindrops Keep Falling...

Many men become quite adept at simply stroking their lover's erogenous zones, say, as you're kissing. You know what I mean – things like simply moving their fingertips back and forth under her hair at the base of her neck, on the back of her arm or on her buttocks. This feels wonderful and reassuring as well as sensuous, but there are so many other ways to touch her and she won't want you to leave any stone unturned.

Here's another touching technique that will make her think you're incredibly sensual. Imagine using your fingertips like little droplets of rain, as if in a 'pitter-patter' pattern of tiny raindrops landing along her skin. This technique feels amazing when you're getting into real foreplay territory, if done right across her pubic mound.

Think of the area about a hand's width below her belly button and about 1.5cm above her clitoris. Let your fingertips alight in a raindrop pattern back and forth across her pubic mound.

I'll tell you this now, but you need to bear in mind the following information for when you touch this area in other ways, as the pubic mound will be mentioned throughout the book. The clitoral region expands out underneath the skin, down her labia, and around her pubic bone. Yes, the clitoris is the tiny 'love bud' located under the clitoral hood but they've now discovered that below the skin of the body of the clitoris, the nerve endings move outward through this region. So when you lightly pitter-patter your fingertips across her pubic bone you send loads of tiny vibrations into her clitoris. This can quite literally drive her mad, particularly if she has a very sensitive clitoris. She'll be begging for penetration but don't give in to her desire just yet! You can use the raindrop technique anywhere she's particularly sensitive.

The Alternator

One of the easiest touching techniques available simply involves alternating your hands. This little trick is best put to use on her larger erogenous zones. It's fantastic for her breasts, her bottom, her belly and her inner thighs. You need to use lashings of lubricant or massage oil, so warm some in your hands. Then if, say, she's lying on her back, start by placing your hands on the area to be massaged – for example, her breasts – and begin this technique. Start to move your hands gently. As one hand gently moves downwards, the other moves upwards. You subtly alternate your hands, passing each other up and down, back and forth. Plant a few kisses on her breasts and then move down to her inner thighs. As you alternate your hands on this area make sure your little finger that passes nearest to her labia gently skims her there to add a teasing sensation.

Swirling

Getting creative when touching your lover's skin isn't that hard if you practise to make perfect! On your inner wrist trace tiny figure of eights and circular swirling patterns. See how wonderful and sensual it feels. Vary the intensity, the speed and the size of the little swirling patterns you make. As you vary your touch, you'll get a good idea of how this might feel on your partner's body.

Using a swirling action is perfect for smaller erogenous zones. If you've started foreplay you could take your partner's hand, turn it over and kiss her inner wrist. Then, while holding her wrist with one hand, do the swirling with the fingertips of your other hand, slowly moving up to the inside of her elbow. She'll probably never have experienced such a lovely delicate swirling sensation.

Other great places for trying swirling include behind her ear lobes as you kiss her lips. Or if you're kissing round her pubic mound and labia, push her legs a bit open and do this tiny figure-of-eight and circular swirling pattern very high up her inner thigh, just where it meets the outside of her labia – she'll find it heaven on earth!

Erotic 8 Massage

Now, for a bigger figure-of-eight technique that will give every bit as much pleasure in a very different way. Your lover needs to be lying on her back or on her stomach for the Erotic 8 Massage. Warm your hands and pour loads of massage oil on them, then start with your hands meeting at her breastbone (above her breasts). Sweep your hands apart and outwards, skimming the sides of her breasts and coming in to meet at her belly button. Then skim them back outwards around the sides of her hips, coming in to meet at the top of her pubic bone.

Repeat this action, in reverse, moving back up her body and coming into her belly button first, then out and around the side of her breasts and meeting at the top of her breastbone. You can keep doing this wonderful, big swirling figure-of-eight movement up and down her body.

However, if you happen to be a bum man, and love the look of her bottom, guide her on to her stomach and do the same starting at her upper back. Sweep around the sides of her ribcage, just skimming the sides of her breasts and meeting your fingertips at her waist. Then skim back outwards, forming the second part of the figure of eight, moving your hands out around her buttocks and meeting just at the base of them, where the upper thighs come together to meet her buttocks. A very sensitive and sexy area!

Eastern Swirl and Poke

This is actually a fabulous kiss but I'm including it here as it's ideal for stimulating the skin on many erogenous zones. Legend has it that great lovers of the East used this kiss to arouse their lover's passion. Amazing sensations are created by alternating the movement of your tongue between a swirling action and a poking action.

Of course, you can begin by using it as a kiss: as you French kiss, start moving your tongue in a swirling action around her tongue and then you gently poke the inside of her mouth with the tip of your tongue. Moving between the swirling and poking arouses a lot of tingling sensations in her mouth.

But let's move on to stimulating her body! Imagine using your tongue in this way on her nipples. First you swirl the tip of your tongue around her nipple's areola and then, subtly and gently, use it to poke her erect nipple. Move between these two sensations and it will feel fabulous to her. Now move down her body to her belly button and swirl around and around the edge of the delicate skin of her belly button. Then gently poke your tongue into her belly button – a much-neglected erogenous zone! You can also use the swirl and poke when she's lying on her stomach and you've traced a line down her back with your tongue to where her buttocks meet to form the cleft at the base of her spine. Swirl this little indented area and then gently poke at it.

To do something incredibly sexy with the swirl and poke technique, make sure she's just come out of a bath or shower so her feet are clean. Then swirl your tongue around the tip of one of her toes before gently poking between her toes. She'll think you're an amazing lover!

Perfectly Sexy Pinching

Tell your lover you're going to pinch her and she may say, 'No way!' But gradually introduce a pinching sensation and she may start to feel incredibly aroused. The best places to pinch are just on the edges of her most sensitive erogenous zones. But the trick is to start with a tender little pinch and gradually build up the sensation between your thumb and forefinger.

Imagine you're kissing her and have been caressing her body. Move your thumb and forefinger to her pubic mound. First run your fingers back and forth over it a couple of times. Then gently pinch the fleshy mound in the centre of the pubic bone. Repeat this, using the pinching action to gently pull up the flesh of the pubic mound. Keep repeating this in a rhythmic action and her clitoris will get extremely stimulated in the most erotic way!

Now, why not try this pinching technique on her inner thighs. By now her legs may be parted because she's feeling so turned on, so you can find the crease where the top of her thigh meets the outer edge of her labia. Again, stroke this area a few times then gently pinch the soft flesh here with your thumb and forefinger. Keep a rhythmic action going. This will increase blood flow to her labia making her feel aroused.

Remember to do this pinching gently unless she specifically asks you to do it with a firmer touch.

Lovely Labial Massage

This brings me nicely to the most wonderful way to arouse her labial area and make her labia swell with desire. Really take charge as a lover here. Even if you're the most gentle of men, and you two have the most sensitive and loving relationship, by far the majority of women love it when a man takes charge at different points during sex.

Imagine you two have been caressing each other and things are getting exciting. Ask her to lie back and part her legs. Make sure your hands are nice and warm and your fingertips are covered with a luscious lubricant. You can give her a labial massage in one of two ways. The first way is to use the fingertips from both of your hands and, beginning at the base of one labia, ever so gently massage up to the top of that labia near to her clitoris. Then move both of your hands to the base of her other labia and again gently massage up to the top. The second way of giving her this massage is to kneel between her legs and use your hands separately on each of her labia. Again, start at the base and gently wiggle your fingers in a massaging motion as you move up both her labia to her clitoris.

There are two key ways to heighten her pleasure during a labial massage. Firstly, you need to keep asking her if you're getting the pressure and firmness correct. She may want a more gentle massage or a firmer fingertip massage. Secondly, you need to keep your fingers well lubricated so they feel heavenly on her labia.

Luscious Lubes

Never underestimate the power of using luscious lubricants to heighten her sensitivity. There are all sorts of lubricants available at adult shops and on the Internet. The wonderful thing about lubricants is that you can both have fun with them and get extra raunchy with them too.

Of course, you can use lubricants anywhere on her body. Make sure you put a big dollop in the middle of your hand and warm it up before you start gently rubbing it over her body. An extra fabulous place to use lubricants is down her labia, over the perineum and up between her buttocks. Yes, if she's aroused (and doesn't have any problem with getting lubricated) her own natural juices will make her vagina and labia moist. However, ask her to relax back while you put an extra big dollop of lubricant on the palm of your hand and warm it up with your other hand. Then you can reach right under her bottom and smooth it in a great big, luscious sweeping action from her buttocks right up over her labia, her clitoris, and on to her pubic mound and lower tummy.

Re-apply more lubricant then slip your hand back under her buttocks and do that big sweeping motion again. By the time you've repeated that a number of times (mind you don't catch her clitoris on the way up with the palm of your hand as she gets aroused), she'll be feeling fantastic. Continue enjoying a luscious lubricant you've chosen throughout sex-play and during penetration.

The Full Four

Think about your hands exploring the whole area of her vagina and perineum. This technique is easy to do and yet so effective in turning her on. Allow all four of the fingertips of one hand to gently relax over her pubic bone, with your thumb relaxing against her inner thigh and the edge of her pubic mound. Your fingertips should be touching/resting against her labia and introitus (the opening to her vagina).

Ensuring you use a delicate touch, start moving your fingertips up and down her labia. They should be well lubricated with your favourite lubricant. After a number of strokes start to gently circle your fingertips – again over this whole area. As she begins to get aroused and lubricated you can go back to the rocking, stroking motion and then allow one or two of your fingertips to slide into her vagina. Once one or two of your fingertips are in her vagina, and the other fingertips are still touching her labia, continue the rocking motion. The fact that your whole masculine hand is gently rocking and circling this area is a huge turn-on.

The Naughty Dog Kiss

Here's another kiss that is also perfect for stimulating her by using it on different parts of her body. You can use this kissing technique on her breasts during foreplay. What you need to do is allow your tongue to relax – think of a dog panting on a hot summer's day! Then starting at the base of her breast you do a big lap that finishes at the tip of her nipple with a gentle flick. Repeat this around the base of her breast placing your tongue further along this area with each lap. This way you stimulate all the skin at the base of her breast with each lap. And as each lap finishes it flicks across a different side of her nipple.

The Naughty Dog can also be used on her inner thigh. As she parts her legs you can lap gently along her inner thigh just glancing the side of her labia with your mouth and tongue. This is such a tease! You're not actually giving her oral sex but she feels on the edge of that pleasure! If she's lying on her stomach and you're giving her a back massage you can also bend over and do the Naughty Dog on the base of her buttocks, lapping up and flicking different areas of the centre of her buttocks.

Venus Vibrations

Vibrators come in all shapes and sizes. If you're not feeling very experimental, and haven't used vibrators, you should simply go for one of the basic penis-shaped ones. Even the basic vibrators usually have a few speed variations from slow to fast. Before you use it on your lover with the following little trick, get to know how it feels on your own hand.

When you've been enjoying a little sex-play get out your lubricant and gently cover her lower tummy and Mons Venus (pubic mound) with it. Now take the vibrator and start with it on its lowest setting. Rather than using the vibrator with the end of it touching her skin, lay it almost flat along her pubic bone and start to move it back and forth so you cover quite a large area with its vibrating side. Vibrating across her pubic mound and lower tummy in this way will drive her nuts because it stimulates the deeper part of the 'clitoral arms'.

The Roman Bath

For a really sensuous experience try this technique. Ask her to share a bath with you. Run a lovely, warm bath with some sensual aromatherapy oil in it, like ylang-ylang or a variation of musk. Slip in first and ask her to get in and sit inside your legs with her back towards you. Make sure she pins her hair up if she has long hair. She's going be the 'Roman Empress' that you carefully bathe and caress.

Begin with a simple pleasure by trickling some warm water from a face cloth down her neck and back. Next, gently kiss the back of her neck with your lips as you slide your arms around her ribcage to her breasts. From this position lightly circle her nipples, stroke the whole of her breasts, and run your fingertips up to her neckline under her chin (a very sensitive erogenous zone) as you continue to nuzzle the back of her neck. Now, let one of your hands drift down between her legs as the other hand cups one of her breasts. She'll be sitting snugly between your legs in the bath so very gently nudge one finger between her thighs to start caressing her clitoral region. Continue to spoil her with erotic kisses and touching as you snuggle her between your thighs. She'll feel incredibly spoilt like a Roman Empress.

Fabulous Fingertips

It's definitely worth investing in a fingertip vibrator! Choose one with a silent/quiet action. These slip on to your forefinger and can reach all sorts of tiny and exciting places that a normal-sized vibrator can't. One delicate area that is under-stimulated is behind the ear lobes. Place a tiny amount of lubricant on the end of the fingertip vibrator. If it has different speeds set it on the lowest. Now, as you kiss her on the lips, gently trace little circular patterns on her ear lobe. Then begin to move the fingertip vibrator into the lovely little area behind her ear lobe at the top of her neck. Continue to make little circling motions as you kiss her.

As you continue to kiss her you could slip the fingertip vibrator down to circle her nipples. Always remember to ask her if she likes the pressure when you are using a vibrator. She may want you to push on it a bit more firmly or pull away slightly from her skin so that the fingertip vibrator just barely glances across her erogenous zones.

The Medieval Necklet Kiss

This kiss is not meant for the lips. It's to stimulate the tender skin around the collarbone and neckline. The name derives from medieval times when fair maidens wore low-cut necklines that revealed their cleavage.

Legend has it that when a knight wanted to seduce a maiden the trick was to plant erotic little kisses, one after the other, along her collarbone above her heaving bosom! This kissing style would tantalise her so that she longed for her knight to reveal her breasts and kiss them, too. Begin at the base of your lover's neck and slowly encircle her neckline with little kisses. Pause between each so that she can feel your breath along her collarbone. It's an incredibly sensual technique.

Luscious Liquids

You can use this fun little tip when sharing any sort of drink with her. The greatest lovers never miss an opportunity to turn an ordinary action into a simple erotic little pleasure. Let's say you're celebrating something with her and sipping champagne. Ask her to tilt her head back slightly as you drip a couple of droplets of champagne into her waiting lips. Then plant a kiss onto her moist lips.

If you're relaxing with a cocktail why not sip some of the cocktail into a straw and then trickle it down her cleavage. Catch the little drips with your tongue and lap at the lovely area between her breasts. Even if you're sharing something like hot chocolate you can turn it into a little pleasure. Check that it has cooled down before spooning some drops into her belly button to lick out.

If you don't want to worry about any spillage or mess why not share a drink while sitting in the bath together. Light a few candles, lean forward and trickle some of your wine or champagne down her breasts to gently lap off.

The Best Biting

As with any pleasure that might involve a little pain, always start extra gently and ask her what she thinks about the technique. Many people bite each other gently, particularly when they reach climax. For some it's a reflex action to bite their lover's shoulder as they reach their orgasm.

The skin should never be broken as the human bite is full of germs! But, that said, it's incredibly erotic to experience some gentle biting. You can begin when you've been kissing her breasts and nipples by ever so gently biting her nipple. When I say gentle, I mean gentle! After you've given her a little nip, sensually ask her what she thought of it. Most women respond to gentle biting when they're getting very excited. The mix of pleasure and a little bit of pain heightens their sense that they are getting near their climax.

You could also turn her over and while caressing her buttocks give her a series of little nips. After you've done a gentle bite, stroke the area with your fingertips before planting a little bite elsewhere.

Discover Her Pleasure Map

Every lover has uncharted territory when it comes to their erogenous zones. Part of the excitement of getting to know your lover is discovering her pleasure zones that have been neglected or rarely touched. One way of discovering her pleasure map is to tell her that you don't want to have full sex at this point but instead, you're going on a journey of discovery!

Ask her to lie back, ensuring she's warm and comfortable. Let her know it's best if she closes her eyes and trusts you as you explore. It almost becomes a sensual game when you ask her to rate from 1 to 10 the different areas that you touch: 1 being the least pleasurable and 10 being the most pleasurable sensation.

Beginning at her scalp, try different stroking and touching techniques and get her feedback. Then continue right down her shoulders and along the sides of her arms. Touch around her fingertips and palms and then up inside her wrist, to her inner elbow and up to her armpit. Now you can move along her ribcage, up across her breasts and down her stomach. Change the style of touch you use and the pressure and speed of your touch. You might decide to simply do one area of her body at a time. Another time you might explore her back and buttocks. And yet another time, her legs, feet and toes.

Sextion Two

Tips for Delicious Oral Sex for Her Pleasure

Oral sex is a fabulous way to give your partner pleasure. But even when it comes to the way people give oral sex, they can get into a rut with the 'same thing always on the menu', so to speak. Bearing in mind that women can orgasm more easily through oral sex, it's a good idea to have lots of tips, tricks and techniques on the menu! Where roughly 30 per cent of women say they can orgasm quite regularly during penetrative sex, that number rises steeply to around 80per cent of women regularly reaching orgasm through oral sex. So if you want to 'up' the likelihood of her reaching her sexual pleasure, definitely sprinkle some of these ideas into your oral sex technique.

The Sexy Sponge Bath

Believe me, she will be completely indebted to you if you take charge of giving her an experience to remember during oral sex. This is an incredibly sensual and erotic technique to use. You could either start your foreplay by doing this or if you've been enjoying foreplay, ask her to lie back and relax. Turn the lighting down low or simply do this by candlelight.

Go to the bathroom and run some warm water into a clean basin. Have a fresh, clean and soft face cloth to the ready. Ask her to part her legs as you give her this sexy sponge bath. Gently stroke her labia and vagina with the clean, warm and wet face cloth. Tell her she looks gorgeous and is going to taste lovely. This will build her confidence, as many women fear that they won't taste fresh during oral sex. Do this as if you're treasuring her most private place. Make her feel that she's the most beautiful woman you've ever seen. After the sponge bath you can begin giving her oral sex.

Loving the Pearl

This technique is only to be used when your partner is highly aroused. It would be too much to try early on in giving her oral pleasure. As a woman gets more aroused she usually becomes less sensitive than at the start of arousal. But this is also fantastic for a woman who *does* like direct clitoral stimulation.

In Loving the Pearl, you can either pull her clitoral hood upwards exposing her clitoris more or not; whatever her preference is. Now take your thumb and index finger and rest them either side of her clitoris. Imagine using small twisting, or back and forth motions, with these two fingers. Gently rub her clitoris between your thumb and index finger with these little motions. As you gradually build the pace ask her how it's feeling. She may want a quicker pace or she may want you to vary your touch from firmer to gentler. When you do it correctly, just as she wants it, this is really like releasing the genie from the magic lamp that you've been rubbing!

Hot and Cold Pleasure! Ice Cubes and Hot Lips

Although this might be a little trick to definitely use in hot summer weather, don't shy off trying it if you're in a nice, warm room together despite it being winter outside. Have a tumbler of ice cubes by the bedside. First, with the warmth of your lips and tongue, lick and kiss her labia for a little while. Then, take an ice cube between your fingertips and trace a line across the sensitive area where her inner thighs meet her outer labia.

Next warm up this area through the heat of your lips and tongue again. Go back to giving her a little oral pleasure before taking the ice cube and gently tracing a line down between her labia this time! Again, warm up this area with the heat of your mouth, gently licking up and down between her lips. Next take the ice cube between your fingertips and trace a line across her pubic mound and circling her clitoral region. Before you start giving her oral pleasure again, warm up this area with your lips and mouth. You can repeat this as many times as she wants. The alternating sensations of the cold ice and your hot lips are very stimulating. Usually going through the sequence once is just the perfect tease before getting down to the fun of bringing her to climax through oral sex.

Worship at Her Altar

This is a wonderful tip for the couple that's not shy around each other. However, she needs to be fairly confident about her body, and about you, to agree to this. If she's not, you definitely need subtle lighting to make her feel more body confident. Also, it may be a good idea to suggest doing this when she still has her knickers or a sexy nightie on so she doesn't feel completely exposed.

At any point in your sex-play you can ask her to stand on the floor. Obviously you want to do this on a carpeted floor for your own comfort. Kneel between her parted legs and give her oral sex from this position. She'll feel incredibly dominant if she's wearing high heels and little else! You can hold on to her buttocks so that you can get the right pressure on her clitoris and vagina. Ask her to hold the back of your head as she stands above you to help guide you with the right pressure. Then enjoy worshipping at her altar!

Intimate Grooming

The most thoughtful lovers build intimacy and trust with their partner. One fantastic technique for doing this is to ask her if you can groom her intimately. The first time you offer to do this should be when you're both feeling affectionate and maybe even a bit turned on. Keep things simple and just suggest gently combing or brushing her pubic hair as she lies back. She's probably never had this offer before! This is a great thing to do before giving oral sex as it gets rid of any stray pubic hairs that get caught in your teeth or at the back of your throat – which is not sexy in the slightest.

Once you've begun to build up more trust you can ask her if you can shave her pubic hair. This sort of sex-play definitely shouldn't be done when you've been drinking or taking recreational drugs. The best time to do it is after she's had a shower or bath and you can gently shave her softened pubic hair. You can simply shave her bikini line as anything more intimate, like a complete shave, should be done in a salon by professional waxing rather than shaving. Shave her gently and very carefully; if she shaves herself from time to time she may use sensitive-skin shaving foam. Show willingness and creativity and ask her what she wants you to do. The fact that you're willing to do something so intimate will make her feel incredibly special.

Come On Over

Here's a trick to give her the best of both worlds while you're giving her oral pleasure. It combines using your finger and tongue for double the fun. If you're lying or kneeling between her legs, begin by simply licking and kissing her. As she gets more and more turned on, introduce your fingertips to your sex-play. Stroke her labia gently as you continue your oral techniques.

Once she's really turned on, slowly slide your index or middle finger into her vagina. You can now begin to stimulate her G-spot with your finger while tickling her clitoris with your tongue. You can find her G-spot in this way: it's located on the front wall of her vagina (think the 'tummy' side of the vagina rather than the 'bottom' side), a couple of inches up. It's a slightly spongy mass of tissue, the size of a small coin. Sex researchers debate the existence of the G-spot as some women claim not to feel extra sensations in this area. However, many do, so it's worth experimenting with your fingertip. Simply stroke this general area as if you're using your index finger to signal someone to 'come on over'. Do it gently as you continue giving her oral pleasure.

Sex By Numbers

Here's a little tip for giving her oral pleasure over her entire body. This is another playful tip to take the seriousness out of your sex life. It's also a great tip to extend your foreplay so you both build more desire. Ask her for one of her lipsticks to use. Make sure it's not her most expensive!

Take the lipstick and draw numbers with it around her body. For example, you might put the number 1 on her neckline, the number 2 on one breast, the number 3 on her other breast, the number 4 on her tummy, the number 5 on her inner thigh, the number 6 on her knee, and so on. After you've made an interesting little trail with these numbers you then have to kiss and lick them in the order they fall. If you don't like the taste of her lipstick (many men don't), you can kiss around these areas – that will be more of a tease for her! Before you go for full sex you can gently use make-up remover on a soft tissue to remove your trail of numbers.

Worship the Triangle

This is another technique to worship your lover in the way she deserves! The best lovers are those who make a woman feel incredibly sexy; this is a technique that's guaranteed to make her feel that way. Again, this is good to use on a woman with a sensitive clitoris.

Ask her to lie on her stomach and arch her bottom upward to give you the access you'll need. This can be done in two ways: either she can have her knees and thighs resting on the edge of her bed so that her body lays across the width of the bed or she can have her head on the pillow, lying down the bed in the usual way, and you can lie between her legs. As you approach her from behind you'll see the 'triangle' formed by her thighs and buttocks. In this position you are able to kiss the sensitive areas of her lower labia, perineum and buttocks. You could also use a dental dam or sturdy cling film and give her a little anal-lingus. This technique is fantastic for lovers who enjoy a more sophisticated oral experience.

Tongue Swirling

Here's a little tip for some sexy tongue action! The tongue is a muscle like any other and needs to be worked out regularly. Occasionally, you should simply swirl it around in your mouth, flick it and lap with it to keep it in tip-top shape for giving amazing oral sex.

Before you use this on your lover, try swirling your tongue across one of your knuckles. Even on your masculine hand you'll feel how wonderful the swirling action is as you go around and around on your knuckle. Do this around her clitoral hood – and if she likes it, on her clitoris directly – and she'll be in absolute heaven! Many men simply lap at the clitoris but if you perfect the swirling technique she'll thank you for it. You could also build up to doing a little figure-of-eight double swirl with your tongue, but that takes some practice. So use your knuckle to practice!

Across the Bridge

This is a wonderful technique for giving her a new sensation. And that's what this book is all about – helping you to create some new sensations that stop things getting boring in bed.

Let's say you're in the middle of foreplay and decide to give her oral sex. When you're ready to go down on her (when the timing feels right), you can gently pull her legs apart. Then move yourself down so that you're lying sideways on to her hips. Rest one of your hands flat on her pubic bone and use this to carefully pull the entire area of the flesh on her pubic mound upwards. This helps to expose her clitoris. You can then use your other hand between her legs to sensually finger her. Now for your tongue – you can lap it sideways across her clitoris creating a whole new feeling for her. That's because usually men lie between a woman's legs in one position or another, and so lap up and over her clitoris. This sideways angle in Across the Bridge is both teasing and pleasing in equal measures!

Raising the Flower

If your lover happens to be a fairly flexible woman this will be a great little trick to try on her. You begin by kneeling between her legs while she's lying on her back. Ask her to raise her legs up to rest her calves on your shoulders. You can now pull her hips slightly off the bed so that her genitals are raised up towards your mouth. You need to wrap one hand around her waist to steady her and you can use your other hand to reach up and stroke her stomach or even fondle her breasts if you can reach them.

Once in this position, you can lick and lap to your heart's content at her clitoris, labia and vagina. An oral sex technique like Raising the Flower is best to try with your lover once she's feeling confident with you because in this position, her 'flower' is on full view to you.

Tongue Joy Vibrator

The market for vibrators continues to grow and gets more creative and varied every year. If you've never tried a tongue joy vibrator then you definitely need to get one for oral pleasure!

This neat little vibrator slips on to your tongue so that during oral sex not only does she feel the warmth and moistness of your lips and tongue but also the fabulous little vibrations from this sex toy. Be creative with it. You could begin by stimulating her perineum – the Tongue Joy feels amazing there. Then move up and over each of her labia in turn. Next you can move your tongue around her pubic mound, back and forth, getting nearer and nearer to her clitoral region. Combine moving between these different little intimate areas to drive her completely crazy.

The Beak

This little tip is ideal for the woman who likes a big sensation in her vagina. How you start is by bringing your fingertips and thumb together in order to form a 'beak' shape. Now turn your hand and palm upwards so that you can apply the beak. You need to use a gentle, circular massage motion with your beak in place at the entrance to her vagina. Imagine swirling it around and around at this entrance before slowly slipping it further and further into her well-lubricated vagina as you stimulate her clitoris with your tongue and lips.

The Beak will give her a full feeling in her vagina while she enjoys your lips and tongue on her clitoris and clitoral region. Make sure your nails are carefully trimmed when you do the Beak – and any time you touch her intimately.

The Pelvic Rub

Her pelvic area has all sorts of interconnections with her genitals. Many lovers don't realise this and so fail to stimulate this area, but when it's caressed and rubbed, it subtly leads to stimulating her clitoris and genitals generally.

Surprise her with this unique knowledge by using the following trick. When she's lying back comfortably and you're going to go down on her, that's the time to try the Pelvic Rub. Think of the area a few inches below her belly button and a couple of inches above her pubic mound. With one hand place your index and middle fingers together and lay them on this pelvic region. Apply a little pressure and slowly massage up and down in circular motions. Keep the massage just to this region; don't let your fingers stray much further. While you're doing this you'll be lying between her legs giving her oral sex, or you can do this in the Across the Bridge position described above. The combination of the Pelvic Rub and oral sex should give her a fantastic climax.

Reach the Peach

This is a really sexy position that will make her feel quite naughty! It's fantastic for women who are body-confident, but you could also encourage a shyer lover to let go and enjoy allowing you to Reach the Peach.

You will be lying back on the bed or on the floor, if it's comfortable. Ask her to kneel above you with her knickers off, or you can use your fingers to pull her knickers to one side. Not only do you get a really hot view of your lover but she has quite a bit of control while you give her oral pleasure. Tell her to feel free to raise herself up and down, skimming her labia along your mouth, by moving with her knees and thighs.

She can turn this into a bit of a game where she tempts you by keeping herself just out of reach of your lips. Of course, you can regain control by clasping your arms around her bottom and pulling her hips to you tightly, especially once she's ready to orgasm.

A Heavenly Handful

This is a sensation she'll probably never have experienced and uses the alternator technique above specifically to get her ready for oral sex! She should be lying comfortably and you should be kneeling above her. Sensuously spread her legs. Now, with lashings of lubricant on your hands, move your fingers together and keep your hands lightly cupped. Using a sensual movement alternate moving your right and left hands up and down. Start at her pubic bone with one hand sweeping down over her labia and inner thighs while the other hand starts from her perineum and sweeps upwards. You should be using gentle but large sweeping movements as your hands pass each other in opposite directions.

Not only is she completely exposed with her legs open arousing you but she'll also be highly aroused by the gentle alternating movements between your hands that cover her entire genital region. It takes a fair amount of trust on her part unless you have the lights down low, or only a couple of candles lit, so she feels you're not staring at her. Unless she gets off on a bit of exhibitionism – then she'll love this technique! Now she'll be ready for you to slip down between her legs and plant kisses where your hands have been stimulating her.

Sitting Pretty

This is a great little trick for enjoying some spontaneous oral sex. Let's say your lover is sitting on the edge of the bed, or on the edge of a chair or sofa. This will give you good access for this technique. After some sex-play, get down and kneel between her legs. Pull her hips towards you so she's sitting on the edge of the bed or chair. Hold her hands and guide them to the back of your head. Tell her that you want her guidance to bring her to ultimate pleasure with her pulling your head into the exact position she wants and keeping the right pressure on.

Now bring your mouth to her and give her some wonderful oral pleasure while she's sitting pretty! Not only is this a great sex trick, particularly if she likes being in control, but it also helps keep your sex life spontaneous. Alternatively, you can use this oral sex trick in the kitchen or bathroom. Help her get up on to the bathroom or kitchen worktop where you have easy access to give her oral pleasure in these new surroundings.

Nose Nuzzling

There's hardly anything raunchier than this little tip when it comes to oral sex! This shows your down-and-dirty side that hopefully she'll love. When you go to give her oral pleasure using whatever technique she enjoys, pause and start nuzzling her labia and clitoris with your nose. Move the tip of your nose in little circles around her clitoris. Then move it up and down between her moist labia. Then go back to licking and kissing her for a while.

You can then restart the nuzzling and tease her with this incredibly erotic sensation. You can quite literally take her breath away by using this intimate technique. She'll feel truly worshipped!

The Stir

Here's a little fingering tip that will heighten her oral pleasure. What you need to do is keep your index and middle finger together. Think about using these in a stirring action.

While you give her oral sex insert these two fingers into her vagina. Then slowly begin this stirring action moving around and around inside her. It's a fantastic fingering technique because whether she's incredibly tight or on the larger size you can make your stirring actions smaller or larger to stimulate all of the sides of her vagina. It feels fabulous because she gets complete internal stimulation with all her vaginal nerve endings touched at some point during your circular stirring motion. And she also gets the external pleasure of you sucking, kissing or licking her clitoris or clitoral region.

Love Bud and Other Oral Sex Nicknames

People get so freaked out about oral sex. They worry about whether they're doing it right, they worry about whether they're doing it for long enough, they worry what it means when their lover starts pressing their head and guiding it this way or that. To take some of the worry out of giving her oral sex, give her a fun or raunchy nickname for her clitoris, vagina or labia.

Use your imagination! You could call her clitoris anything from the 'love bud' to the 'mouse's nose'. I've heard of people calling their lover's vagina anything from the 'hot hole' to 'Mandy'! And, of course, the labia are often nicknamed 'hot lips' or 'rose-petal'. Be creative and make it something meaningful to both of you to laugh about but obviously don't choose anything offensive that in any way implies that she looks unattractive. So, think before you speak her new nickname.

Down Under

Here is an unusual position for oral sex that will make her think you're a skilled lover – always a good thing! This is how you do it: imagine she's lying on her back on your bed completely relaxed as you two enjoy some caressing. Ask her to 'shimmy down' a little so her head's off the pillow and her feet are near the bottom of the bed. Now you move from lying side-by-side with her, 180 degrees, so essentially your head is towards her feet and your feet rest where the pillow is.

In this position you can rest gently over her abdomen with your head at her pelvis. From here you can create entirely new sensations through oral sex. You'll be licking downwards, gently over her clitoris. This is a particularly great option for a woman that's extra sensitive in the clitoral region as you're going downwards over the clitoral hood so it protects her clitoris from direct stimulation. Moving slightly lower down you can reach your tongue down further and stroke her labia and even her perineum in Down Under.

Sextion Three

Tips to Liven Up Sex Positions for Her

Many people make the mistake of assuming that just because they know lots of different positions it must make them a great lover. What separates a great lover from a merely good lover is the one who gets creative when in different sex positions. Even the addition of the smallest tip or technique, done sensuously, will add to a sex position and can lead to mind-blowing orgasms.

Perfect Penis Action

Don't forget that your penis is an amazing thing! It's bendy even when erect and this flexibility can be used to wonderful effect. Once penetration starts, many men simply thrust back and forth like a jackhammer. They may be a slow jackhammer and build her desire through a slow thrusting movement. Or they may be a fast and fierce jackhammer, but the thrusting motion remains the same: in and out, in and out and so on. This can be incredibly pleasurable for both partners and, of course, as long as she's getting enough clitoral stimulation both may end up having great climaxes this way.

However, just a little bit of ingenuity that uses your natural flexibility can change the thrusting in any sex position into an erotic experience. Imagine your penis as a great, big mixing spoon and when you're penetrating her, move it around and around in a swirling, circular motion inside her. You do this as if you're stirring her inside with your penis. This feels sensational inside her. Build up your hip flexibility with gentle rotations of your hips every time you're in the shower. This little bit of pre-planning will blow her mind in bed.

Doggy Style Delight

Doggy style is a sizzling position favoured by many couples. It's quite earthy and she can get G-spot stimulation as well as clitoral stimulation by either pleasuring herself during thrusting, or you can reach around and pleasure her clitoris to bring her to climax.

A fantastic little tip is to add in the fingertip vibrator I've already mentioned earlier. Slip it onto your finger before you get into doggy style. Once you start penetrating her and you've found your centre of balance (important to doggy style as many men find they slip out if they're not quite balanced), reach around with that finger and stroke just below her belly button with every thrust. After a few of these strokes, move it down to her lower pubic mound, just above her clitoris, and hold it there. She should enjoy the vibrating sensations as you're thrusting. But always check that it's right for her, as she may want you to start circling her clitoris with it or to hold it in a stationary position very near to her clitoris.

Reverse Missionary Tickle

The Reverse Missionary position is, as it says, with the woman lying on top of the man with his legs in between hers. This can be a very slow and sensuous position to have sex in. It doesn't require a lot of effort so is particularly nice to enjoy after a late night or when, for whatever reason, you don't have much energy.

However, one fantastic and easy-to-use tip in this position involves a little bit of creative finger play. Normally, as your lover moves on top of you, you might reach around and hold her buttocks with both of your hands. But as you do this, reach both sets of fingers down to her perineum and lower labia area. Gently tickle this rarely touched erogenous zone with your fingertips. This gives three of her pleasure zones stimulation: her clitoral region will be moving against your pubic bone, you'll be inside her, and you'll be stimulating this lower vaginal area. This can really heighten her orgasm!

Coital Alignment Bliss

The CAT or Coital Alignment Technique is a fantastic position to use, particularly if she finds reaching orgasm difficult. As in the Reverse Missionary she's on top. However, she should shimmy an inch up so that she can grind her clitoris into your pubic bone. She can either have her legs in-between yours or outside yours, or this can be done in the Classic Missionary position with you on top. However, from what people report to me, the CAT works best with her on top. The beauty of this position is that she can control the pressure and friction and get exactly the clitoral stimulation she needs to reach climax.

To give added pleasure, you can slip your fingers between your two pubic areas and insert one, two or more fingers there. Ask her what feels best. Now you can apply gentle circular pressure, about three inches below her belly button, to this area. As she's moving her clitoris against your pubic bone, and you're stimulating with your fingers between your two bodies, slightly above her pubic mound, she'll get immense pleasure.

Sensual Spoons

The Spoons position is where you're both lying on your sides and you're behind her. Her back is facing your chest so you rest together like two spoons in a drawer. As with the Reverse Missionary this is a very relaxing position that many couples enjoy. It's both affectionate and sexy. You can hold on to her and she can even reach her upper arm back and around you to ensure you don't slip out during penetration.

A wonderful technique to enhance the Spoons position is where you reach around and begin by caressing her pubic mound during thrusting. Then, open up your fingers so that your index and middle fingers form a sort of V-sign. Slip this down on either side of her clitoris. With a little pressure, but not too much, hold her labia with your V-sign and as your bodies move, this position will stimulate her whole clitoral region.

Erotic Split the Whisker

A great position that requires only a little bit of flexibility is the Split the Whisker position. You need to crouch on your knees as she lies on her back. Help her rest one of her legs on your shoulder. You can then hold her hips, thighs or knees in order to keep control during thrusting so you don't slip out of her. You can do this position in bed or on the floor, for as long as you can crouch comfortably.

This position is very erotic as you can see her labia and vagina – most men find this incredibly arousing. The sexually confident woman feels very sexy in this position. A little tip to liven things up is to ask her to gently play with her clitoris as you watch! Because you're kneeling, and pulling her into you, at least one of her hands can be free to do this. Tell her to let go and enjoy fingering herself as you continue to thrust.

Embrace All of Me

This is a great position if you're feeling romantic and loved-up and want to look into each other's eyes. It's called the Lover's Embrace and you lie on your sides facing each other. What she has to do is lift her upper thigh to allow you to penetrate her. She can wrap her upper leg around the back of your leg. You can both wrap your arms around each other and if she moves her upper leg slightly lower or slightly higher, it varies the pressure on penetration.

One little trick to make the Lover's Embrace position extra special is to reach around and caress her lower back. As she relaxes and you thrust, you can then move your hand to stroke the cleft above her buttocks. This is another one of those little-stimulated areas that feels heavenly when touched. Continue penetration and stroking this cleft. Have some lubricant handy so your fingers can really slip around this area, and she'll love it.

Spinner Winner

Here's a handy little technique to use on her if she enjoys a little bit of rough play. Help her to move into the Spinner position. In this position, you lie flat on your back and she mounts you but faces your feet. She needs to move into this position carefully as it will bend your penis back slightly. She's pretty much in control and can bounce up and down on your penis, gently at first, and then building to a more vigorous movement. 'Bum men' love this position as you get a good view of her bottom!

Ask her to keep a nice slow rhythm – or go back to one if she's started to move more vigorously – and now it's time for a little bit of rough play where you pull her hair gently from behind. This is an ideal technique if you to enjoy a bit of role play – holding on to her hair you can pretend to be a dominant person (for example, the cowboy who's 'taming' her, or the policeman who's asked for sex instead of arresting her) and she's your sex slave.

Sex Up the Straddle

The Straddle is an inventive position for spontaneous sex. Imagine that you've been sitting on the edge of the bed, or even on a sofa, and you two have been flirting or talking about sex and getting aroused. She can pull up her skirt and drop her knickers or pull off her trousers and come and straddle you. With her knees bent on either side of you, she'll get support from the edge of the bed or sofa. She can hold on to your shoulders for added support and you reach around her waist. Depending on your strength and her flexibility, movement can either be slow and sensual or a bit more vigorous.

For a touch of added pleasure in this position you can give her extra stimulation by reaching around and caressing her bottom instead of holding on to her waistline. Really grip each one of her buttocks between your two hands and squeeze them with every one of your thrusts. Mind you, only squeeze as hard as she likes. The contrast between you squeezing her buttocks and the thrusting of your penis will feel fantastic to her. Or, if she has big breasts, and she's moving with a slow and sensual pace, ask her to arch her back so that you can suck her nipples during the Straddle.

Recharge the Resting Dog

From the Doggy position you can move to the Resting Dog. This is where she eases forwards from leaning on her hands and slips down on to the bed so that her forearms rest on the mattress. This naturally arches her hips and pelvis back up to you even further. If she's G-spot sensitive it means she gets a really deep stimulation of this area that will feel fantastic.

Once in the Resting Dog try this tip to stimulate extra sensations. Gently and sensually slap her bottom as you have such good access to it. Obviously don't do this out of the blue but say to her something like, 'I'd love to give your beautiful bottom a little slap!' Make it a nice, slow technique where you first slap one side of her bottom and then the other. You can give her a little slap with each thrust. If she likes a bit of slap and tickle, she'll love this!

Hands On the Mount

The Mount is for the couple who like to be inventive with their sex positions – and who are flexible. Help her ease herself up on to the back of a big (and very sturdy) armchair. You can kiss and caress in this position before you slip in between her legs. Now, hold her hips firmly as she balances and then begin penetration. It's easy to get aroused by the fact that you're doing quite a raunchy position rather than the same old tried-and-tested position.

Once you've got into the rhythm of thrusting in this position and feel steady on your feet continue holding her hips or waist with one hand. Let go with the other hand and swirl it around one of her breasts. Alternate swirling and caressing her breasts with your hand until you both reach climax.

The Lustful Love Knot

This is another great position to try, especially if she loves to have her breasts stimulated. She needs to be fairly flexible to enjoy the Love Knot position. You need to sit in a chair, or securely on the edge of a bed or sofa. Pull her towards you and ask her to sit astride you but with her back towards your chest. Once securely in this position, and you've done a little bit of thrusting, she then twists from the waist up, so that you can nuzzle her neck and kiss her, if she's that flexible. She can then reach her arms behind her, over her shoulders, and wrap them around your neck. Continue to thrust very gently in this position. The way she arches and twists her back adds extra pressure and friction to penetration.

Pause after some thrusting and reach around her ribs, cupping your hands under both of her breasts. Gently caress them and tweak her nipples before you restart thrusting. As this is a position for advanced lovers you'll know that taking your time between thrusting to stimulate other erogenous zones can give enormous satisfaction. And in this position, her breasts are the perfect erogenous zone to take time over!

Crank Up the Missionary

The Classic Missionary position is with the man lying on top of her and in-between her legs. It's very satisfying to many couples, particularly when they add in a little extra technique to make it more interesting.

I think the most fabulous tip for invigorating and cranking up the sensuality of the Missionary is done very simply. All you have to do is reach round with your hand, under one of her buttocks, to tease her perineum and the lower part of her labia.

She can bend her leg at the knee slightly, lifting this buttock to give you access.

The Sexy Sling

Standing positions are considered more risqué and exciting for many couples than lying or sitting positions. Let's say you've been kissing or caressing and things are hotting up. Move her so that she can lean against a wall and slip one of your arms underneath one of her knees. If she's much shorter than you, it may be easier for you to enter her if she has high heels on. Otherwise you can bend your knees as you angle yourself into her. This is the Sling position.

Here's a trick to spice it up. As you gently thrust in this position, raise her knee a little bit higher to really open up her vagina. Now, make sure she's leaning firmly back against the wall for support and with your free hand (it's probably been supporting you against the wall or you've had it wrapped around her waist) massage her pubic mound as you slow down your thrusting. Her clitoris will be fairly well exposed and you can gently circle it with your fingers as you continue your slow thrusts. This will give her incredibly exciting sensations!

Perk Up the Puppet

The Puppet position is another one that's perfect for having a great view of her bottom, so if you're a 'a bum man' you'll love this! If you've been standing and fondling each other, ask her to turn around. Or, as with all standing positions, if you've been lying down and enjoying foreplay you can still suggest standing up – never be worried about getting a little creative! Then ask her to bend gently from her waist. If she's very flexible she can rest her fingertips on the ground. If she's not so flexible, make sure she bends towards a sofa, chair or even the wall so she can rest her hands on this. This is the Puppet and you can control the thrusting during it. She just relaxes and enjoys the sensations.

While supporting her waist with one hand, put your other hand to good use with lovely, slow circular massage motions around her buttock. Alternate these between sensual circles and little fingertip ripples around her bottom. You can then change hands, swapping over to use your other hand with these motions.

Stand and Deliver Sexiness

This standing position is great for a role play. You can pretend you're a detective who's arresting her and have asked her to face the wall. You then ease her skirt up and her knickers down! With her hands pressed into the wall she supports herself firmly while you take her from behind and are in control of penetration.

The perfect little tip to add to the Stand and Deliver position is to put your fingertips to good use. Carefully reach around her hips and use your fingertips to caress her clitoris as you continue to thrust. Ask her what feels best: does she want you to rub lightly across her lower pubic mound or does she want you to circle around her clitoris? Whatever she chooses will add a whole extra dimension to this position.

69 Is Fine

If you fancy some oral pleasure before moving into full penetration, the 69 position is fantastic. Sixty-nine is where you lie head-to-toe and give each other oral pleasure: your head resting between her thighs and her head resting at your thighs, giving her access to your

penis. Once you've enjoyed this relaxed side-by-side 69 then ask
her to kneel over you to continue.

When her bottom is above you, you can put your hands to good
use in this technique. Caress her buttocks with one hand while
you caress her clitoral region with the other. Your mouth is in-
between giving her fantastic oral pleasure while your hands are
working either side. You can bring her to climax before you start
penetration a 'second time around' or if you don't bring her to
climax this way, she'll be hugely turned on and ready for
penetration whenever you are. When you're ready to move her
into a position for penetration, place each hand firmly in place –
one on her bottom and the other at her clitoral region – and ease
her over. It's a wonderful feeling for her when you take control
like this.

The Sensuous Staging Post

As far as positions go, the Staging Post is one of the ones where you
need to be flexible. You might be on the bed enjoying foreplay and
move into it. You might have started to undress each other, and be
standing up, and then move into it. She kneels with one knee on the
bed and her other leg stays planted on the floor. With one hand she
can hold on to the bedhead and gently rest the other on the bed
itself. You stand behind her and hold on to her waist while you
begin penetration.

You can enjoy the Staging Post right through to climax or move
on to the bed to finish each other off. While you're in this position
though, a little extra trick is to move your hands from her waist up
under her breasts and cup them. From cupping them you can also
caress and massage them. Also, why not nuzzle the back of her neck
and ears with your nose and lips?

Missionary Satisfaction

As the Missionary position is so popular with many couples, here's an extra little tip to give her more pleasure during it. As you thrust with your hips, nuzzle your lips against her ear and suck her ear lobe gently. You can alternate the sensation between sucking it and gently licking it. Be careful you don't breathe too heavily into her ear – that can be unpleasant!

Next, try this little trick to tease and tempt her. Raise yourself up on your arms so that you can look straight in her eyes and then slowly withdraw your penis from her vagina. Don't take it all the way out – only halfway. Pause and then thrust it in again. Repeat this so that you tease her by withdrawing partly from her. Then you again resume thrusting. This is a fabulous little trick to heighten her desire for you.

Girls Get Good Sex On Top

A favourite position with many women is Girls On Top. This is where she sits on top of you and facing you. It gives her lots of control. She can raise herself up and down with her feet, if her legs are bent so that her feet are flat on the mattress either side of your hips. Or, as she straddles your hips, her knees can be bent so her lower legs are flat on the bed. She can bend forward to kiss you and then straighten up again.

It's a fantastic position for men who love breasts! Use this little trick to give her extra pleasure – reach out with both hands and with your fingertips gently take her nipples and squeeze and pinch them. Always ask how firm she wants the pressure to be. You can continue to rock or lift yourself up and down during penetration and alternate holding on to her thighs or hips while stimulating her nipples.

The Racy Rocking Chair

The Rocking Chair position is slightly demanding so you need to have some strength and flexibility. This position is fantastic to move into from any rear-entry position, like Doggy style. You're behind her and you rest on your knees with your legs folded beneath you. Keep your upper body upright. She slides her whole bottom and hips back over your thighs, which means she can push her buttocks and vagina right up on to your pelvis. Ask her to bend her legs so that her calves can wrap around gripping the sides of your bent legs. Or, she can sit with her knees bent towards her chest and her feet and toes are down in front of your knees pushing into the mattress. You're definitely in control as you hold her steady and rock her hips gently while you're inside her. It gives you a very subtle and erotic sensation. It's also a good position to use on a carpeted floor as well as a bed.

Once you're well balanced and into the rocking motion, here's a little trick – reach around so that you can gently touch her clitoris with one hand while gently gripping and squeezing her buttocks with the other. Or, if you feel your balance isn't good enough, alternate doing these two little moves, one at a time.

Sextion Four

Tips for Enhancing Her Sexual Fantasies

We tend to assume that women don't think about sexual fantasies as much as men do, but that's certainly not true! Some women may be a touch shyer and more inhibited about sharing their sexual fantasies but they are just as creative, sexy and raunchy as men when it comes to what they fantasise about doing. The following tips, tricks and techniques will help her get the most out of her fantasy life. By helping her put them to good use you'll help her to boost her sexual confidence when it comes to the fantasy part of your sex life.

Strangers in the Night

One of my top recommended fantasies is Strangers in the Night. It's very easy to set up and she'll really enjoy it. Send her a sexy email asking her to meet you for a rendezvous at a bar that neither of you has ever been to. In your email, tell her that you're going to pretend to be a sexy stranger who chats her up. Go into a little detail but don't tell her things like what name you will use, to keep you as a mysterious stranger.

When you both arrive at the rendezvous really get into some

fantasy play. Give her 'the eye' and move up to her and tell her how beautiful she is. This is the moment to say all the seductive or even dirty things you've fantasised about saying to a beautiful stranger. You can even take on a slightly different personality to make this fantasy sex-play extra powerful. After you buy her a drink continue the fantasy as you flirt outrageously. The next step is to suggest a one-night stand by telling her you'll do everything her heart desires. Believe me, when you get back home you two will have sizzling sex that night!

Fantasy Surprise

Here's a fun technique that involves a little fantasy gameplay. Ask her to jot down, on separate pieces of notepaper, five different fantasies she has. She can even write a little scenario for each if she wants to give you more detail. Ask her to fold up the pieces of paper and mix them up and then you must choose one.

Now it's up to you to surprise her by going into that fantasy role and pretending to be the fantasy character she dreams of. For example, the piece of paper might say that you're a sexy neighbour who calls round for coffee. You can immediately start making conversation along those lines. You'll be surprised how easy it is to get into this sort of fantasy chat. She'll love this technique because although she gives you the fantasy scenarios you then have to run with them and create the fantasy.

Drama Queen

Lovers can get incredibly selfish when it comes to fantasy play if they're not careful. Because they're so 'into' their fantasy – like thinking of the sexy Hollywood star they lust after – they forget that it might be off-putting to their partner. It only takes a little thought and tact to avoid someone being turned off by fantasy play, so you need to make sure you don't put your foot in it and suggest that she pretends to be Angelina Jolie!

Instead, you can turn her into a drama queen and ask her to be centre-stage in your fantasy or her own fantasy. Let's say you do fancy Angelina Jolie. You could turn this to your advantage and satisfy your lover by suggesting that you make Angelina wait while she watches you two make love! Then, if you're lucky you might get some fantasy chat about a threesome with Angelina.

You could also ask her if she fantasises about a particular movie star, like Brad Pitt or Orlando Bloom. Then a sexy little tip to get her to open up to fantasy play is to ask if you and her favourite star could feature in a raunchy fantasy. You may find her inner Sex Goddess is unleashed when such fantasy chat lets her get you and Brad or Orlando (or whoever she fantasises about) both pleasuring her.

Fantasy Clothing

Many people feel daunted by full role plays where you get all the outfits and other gear required to fully play out a fantasy. But one great tip to use that will enhance the enjoyment both of you get from fantasy play, is to buy her one piece of the outfit that would go with the fantasy of her dreams!

Let's say she's always fantasised about being a stripper or lap dancer in a club. Many women fantasise about being an erotic temptress – just look at the popularity of burlesque revivalist Dita von Teese. What you could do is buy her one beaded or sequinned bra or a peek-a-boo bra from an adult shop. Wrap it up and give it to her with a note saying she'll look gorgeous in it as she pretends to be the lap dancer she fantasises of being and the sexy tease of your dreams.

Bedtime Story

This is a fun way to indulge in a little fantasy sex-play. It will also give her the courage to tell you some of her fantasy desires. What you do is suggest to her that you play a little fantasy game. You're going to say the first part of a fantasy that you have. For example, you might say: 'I saw a fire engine racing through town today and it got me thinking about what firemen might get up to with the women they save. If I was a fireman and I met you after putting out a fire on your stove, I'd definitely want to get into your knickers.' Then ask her to say what she would like to happen next in this fantasy scenario.

This technique means that you both have equal input into the fantasy story as it develops. It can give you both a little extra sexual confidence since neither of you are responsible for the whole fantasy, and you can end up incredibly turned on by concocting a fantasy storyline together.

You both continue to take turns creating a fantasy story as you go along. Listen carefully to what she suggests in her part of a fantasy so you can get clues about what really turns her on.

Playing Porn Stars

Whether you and your partner are really into porn or not, people have a natural curiosity about getting sexy in front of a camera. You can get up to all sorts of fantasy action by taking pictures or home movies of yourself with a difference.

You can take turns being the director and telling your porn star what position to get into. You might also find that she feels more freedom while playing being a porn star and is willing to try new positions and techniques 'for the camera'.

A huge tip is that people often forget about home lighting and positioning each other in a sexy way. You may shoot a whole home movie only to find that you can't make out any of the sexy detail because of poor lighting or that she looks like an elephant because you filmed her from a bad angle – and that's not sexy!

A word of warning though – if your relationship is on shaky ground make sure you destroy any video or photographic footage of yourselves playing porn stars. I've heard of numerous cases of disgruntled ex-lovers posting such footage on the Internet – if it can happen to Paris Hilton it can certainly happen to you!

Knock, Knock, Who's There?

A sexy little tip to try that takes no effort at all (and we love effort-free tips!), is to play fantasy Knock, Knock. If you're feeling sexy as you arrive at the home you two share, or to her place for the evening, put into action a fantasy Knock, Knock.

Text her to say she's got to ask 'Who's there?' when you arrive. Then think of her favourite fantasy – maybe it's about the deliveryman or one involving her favourite celebrity. When she asks who's at the door, you answer as her fantasy person. She can let you in and you pretend you're talking to her in that role, say, as the sexy deliveryman or Brad Pitt (yes, Brad is on my mind!). You can have fun for the rest of the evening dipping in and out of this fantasy.

It's in the Detail!

Never underestimate the importance of a little bit of delicious detail when it comes to fantasy chat. Because you might feel uneasy about introducing some topics to her when you're thinking about fantasies, what you can do is sprinkle in lots of little details at the beginning of a fantasy theme that will grab her attention and hopefully she'll enjoy the fantasy you want to discuss with her.

For example, if you're dying to share your fantasy about being a dirty police detective who wants to have his wicked way with her, make sure you begin by describing how hunky you'd be, with rippling muscles. Maybe you'd be wearing a slick blazer and sexy dark glasses. You'd act the 'big I am' and be a bit full of yourself as a senior detective. You'd come up to her, question her, and flick open the top button on her blouse. Then you'd allow your fingertips to skim against her nipples as they're pulled tight under her blouse, and so on. I think you get my meaning!

Sprinkle Conversation with Fantasy Ideas

It is the creative and spontaneous lover who gets the most sex. When something mundane happens, like the tap starts leaking in the kitchen, then say to her how you'd like to be her 'handyman' and fix more than her taps.

By taking an everyday event and sprinkling some fantasy ideas into a conversation about it, you may end up rolling into bed when you least expect it!

Hot Fantasy Dice!

This fun sex game will give you hours of pleasure with your sexual fantasies. You need only one dice to play it. Snuggle up together and write down on a notepad a different fantasy scenario corresponding to one number on each side of the dice. Let's say that if you roll a number one it equals a fantasy where you're a lifeguard who saves her in some dangerous waves. If you roll a number two it means you share a fantasy where you're a bank robber who takes her hostage but then seduces her. And so on.

Then you allow her to roll the dice and you have to describe to her how the fantasy corresponding to that number would play out.

Sextion Five

All Sorts of Tempting Tips
for Her Pleasure

There are unlimited ways to give your lover extra pleasure with little tips, tricks and techniques. Sometimes the best new things to try involve everyday activities that you can make more erotic for her pleasure. There are many little creative tips that can arouse her in ways she's never experienced. Here are a few to surprise her with.

Fabulous Fingers and Toes

In my book *Sensational Sex – The Revolutionary Guide to Sexual Pleasure and Fulfilment*, I first mentioned SEPs – Simple Erotic Pleasures. These were little things that could give a great deal of pleasure to your lover.

Try this classic SEP technique – offer to paint her finger or toenails. After she's cleaned off any nail varnish she's wearing, you can tenderly take each finger between your fingertips and paint the polish on. Heighten her pleasure by gently stroking each of her fingers in turn. And, if she's happy to allow you, then do the same to her toes. Some women are a little bit funny about their feet, thinking they're ugly, but toes are full of sensitive nerve endings. They will respond beautifully to your touch. It's so erotic to be treated this gently by a man, and she will love this.

Tether Me

There are all sorts of ways to put bondage to good use. You don't have to be bondage and domination experts and even if you're not really into bondage, you may simply want to try a little bit. Here's a fun trick to try.

Take a silky dressing-gown cord or one of your neckties and get her to lie on her side comfortably on the bed. Ask her to move her arms back so that you can gently tie her elbows together. She may need some pillows to cushion her body on the bed. Now for the fabulous part – pulling her elbows back like this helps to push her breasts outwards. While facing her on the bed this gives you fantastic access to caress them, lick them and kiss them while she feels restrained by her elbows.

You can also do this with her sitting in a chair and just slipping a silky tie around her elbows to bind them gently together. Never leave anyone tied up and tie anything you use (for example, cord, necktie or soft rope) in a bow – not a knot!

Find Her Ear-otic Zone

Research shows that music really does affect our mood. Just as you might feel like dancing to something lively, you can also use music to seduce her. An easy way to do this is to make a CD of all her favourite love songs. Surprise her by slipping it on to the CD player and caressing and kissing her while it plays. Your thoughtfulness will definitely touch her and put her in the mood for seduction.

Another little tip is to make sure you pay plenty of attention to her ear lobes and the spot just behind them on her upper neck. The ancient Chinese believed that the ear lobe contains a pleasure line. As you kiss her lips, make sure you pulsate your fingers (with a gentle squeezing action) as you caress her ear lobe. Then, continue heightening her ear-otic pleasure of this area by swirling the edges of your lips (they should be relaxed) around and around behind her ear lobe. Absolute bliss!

Lip Lust

A sensational tip to add to the sensitivity of her lips that is done with your fingertips. When you've been kissing her, move your head away and rest it on her shoulder. Then put your index and middle fingers together and place the tips of them on her lips. Next gently start to circle them so they give her lips a new sensation.

Like the inner wrist technique described earlier, this is a good one to practise first on your own lips with your fingertips. You'll see what I mean by the way they feel on your lips. You can then alternate kissing her with touching her lips with your fingertips. After your fingertips have touched her lips, lick them and as you start kissing her again with your lips, move those two moist fingers on to her nipples. Now holding the two fingers together, gently circle them on the tips of her nipples.

Give Her an Adrenalin Thrill

Research suggests that when adrenalin is pumping around your body you'll experience a more intense orgasm. You can take advantage of this natural physical state by watching a scary or thrilling film together.

Since the advent of movies, men have used this classic ploy to get the woman in their life a little scared and clinging on to them. They can play at being the 'big, brave man' who will protect her. Once you two have watched a good thriller or scary movie then it's time to seduce her while her adrenalin is pumping. The great thing about sex after something like that is it puts the scary movie out of your mind while you concentrate on your sexual pleasure.

Sexy Stockings

Most men and women love old-fashioned stockings. Men think they look fabulously sexy and women say they feel sexy when they can be bothered to put them on! If she's gone to the trouble to slip into some sexy stockings for your pleasure then use this tip to turn her on. After you two have enjoyed some foreplay and it's time for those stockings and suspenders to come off, then unclip the stockings from the suspenders. This works equally well if they're hold-up stockings – the kind that don't need suspenders.

Now, very slowly begin to slip her stockings down and as you do so kiss along the path they take with your lips. Begin at her upper thigh and inch-by-inch, as you roll down the stockings, plant tender little kisses on her. She'll love this erotic trick and will probably be happy to slip on stockings whenever you ask.

Sexy Hairdresser

As far as SEPs go, you can't go wrong with this tip. When I've suggested this to people to try with their lover, they often don't 'get it' at first. They don't see how it's going to be sexy or erotic. But after trying it, they report back to me about what a fantastic tip it was!

The next time she wants to wash her hair offer to do it for her. Make sure she's really comfortable in a well-cushioned chair at the sink or by the bath. Or, if you have a showerhead in your bath, you can kneel by the bath while she relaxes in it as you wash her hair. Take your time and think about the Raindrop Fingertip technique I described earlier. Gently run your fingers from the top of her scalp down through her hair as you rinse it with warm water. Then, add the shampoo and keep stroking it sensuously as you work the shampoo gently through her hair. Rinse it through carefully with warm water and ask her to sit up so you can help her pat it dry and comb it out. Then you can wrap her hair up in a towel or she can dry it off before joining you in bed. With such erotic treatment you will stimulate all sorts of wonderful sensations in her.

The Bra Strap Flick

People can get pretty clumsy when they try to undress their lover, usually because they feel they're all 'fingers and thumbs'. Or, sometimes they feel nervous about undressing their partner and making a hash of it. But it's a really sexy thing to help your partner undress and all you need to do is take your time – there's no rush.

Here's a little trick to do when you're helping her out of her bra. Having offered to undo it, move around behind her to unclip it. Before you undo it (and then after you've undone it, too), gently flick the straps of her bra against her skin. I mean gently! Think of it as if you were simply flicking her skin in a gentle and loving way with your fingertips. If she's a woman who enjoys any sort of gentle (or not so gentle!) spanking or pinching she'll enjoy this. If you have any doubt about whether she'll like this, then ask her if you can gently flick the straps of her bra against her skin and reassure her that you will 'kiss it better' then plunge in with little kisses.

Exciting Climax

People enjoy feeling all sorts of stimulation at the moment of climax. Some love to feel their partner hold them tight. Some love their partner to touch them in a certain way as they orgasm. And others find letting out a good scream of pleasure heightens the experience.

Here's a little trick to heighten her orgasm. Ask her if she'd like a little bit of a spank on the bottom as she reaches her peak. With a little spank on the bottom at this moment you heighten the pain-pleasure experience. This is where a little bit of pain – and unless you're really into spanking, I do mean a little bit – enhances the sense of pleasure because of the difference between the two sensations. More on these sorts of pleasures in coming tips!

Breast Appeal

The majority of men have a 'thing' for women's breasts. And they give their lover's breasts loads of attention at the beginning of foreplay but then forget about them. You really miss a trick by stopping stimulating them, particularly when she's near her climax. What some men don't realise is that they can truly enhance her orgasm by re-stimulating her breasts at that point.

If you really want to please her then put aside your own pleasure when you know she's coming towards hers. Begin to caress and kiss her nipples again at this moment. And if you're giving her oral pleasure, then reach one hand up to pull at them, and tease them while she orgasms.

Taste Me

Here's a super hot tip to try during penetration. Not only will you come across as a skilled and sophisticated lover but it's very earthy too. When you've been enjoying penetration, and after a number of thrusts, withdraw from her and whisper how you'd like to taste her. Move your head down her body and then kiss her labia gently before starting penetration again.

Honestly, she'll be swept away by the sense that you want to taste her during sex! This can really boost a woman's confidence, as so many get hung up about the way they taste. You can even repeat this trick after you've started thrusting again by withdrawing from her for a second time and heading down south to savour her.

Part Two

Tips, Tricks and Techniques to Tempt Him With

Sextion One

Let Your Fingers Do the Walking – Sexy Touching Tips

Men may well have about half the number of nerve endings that women have in their skin but their skins are still receptive to sensual pleasure. So never underestimate the pleasure you can give a man through his sense of touch. And if his senses have been a bit dulled through neglect, once you re-stimulate a man's body with different touching tips, tricks and techniques, they find they can have so much more sexual enjoyment.

Buff Him Up

If there's one thing the man in your life probably hasn't done, it's to exfoliate his skin. Although there are now all sorts of skin products on sale for men, it's still only a minority of them who will try some out. Tell him you want to enhance his sense of touch and offer to exfoliate his chest and neck area.

Turn it into a SEP – Simple Erotic Pleasure. You can ask him to lie back on a soft, warm towel on the bed, or you can do it when showering with him. Take the exfoliating scrub, rub it between your fingertips and then gently circle the skin on his chest and neck area with it. Use a soft face cloth and warm water to rinse it off. As you make the small circular movements, tell him a few things, like how gorgeous his skin is and how wonderful it will feel when it's done. Whenever you kiss these areas during foreplay it will feel far more sensitive to him.

Lashings of Lubricant for Him

This is a fun little trick that will make you seem like a complete sex vixen to him! Ask him to lie back and dribble some luscious lubricant on to his chest. Really spread it around with your fingertips. Then show him how creative you are and take a body brush, preferably a soft-bristle one, or a clean kitchen basting brush, and gently swish it back and forth through the lubricant.

The brush will give a completely different sensation to the touch of your fingertips and will help to stimulate all sorts of nerve endings. You can then swap back to using your fingertips, swirling them across his pectoral muscles, down around his ribcage, and up around his shoulders. Again, give him loving little compliments to enhance this trick, like saying how gorgeous his chest is.

Thai Hair Massage

Thailand is notorious for its sex trade. Thankfully it's not all seedy and sordid and there are some high quality erotic experiences that the Thai masseuses give their clients. One of these is the Thai Hair Massage.

You can use this technique on him at the beginning of foreplay or later on to slow things down, as it's a very sensual experience, but not one that will bring him to climax unless he has a hair fetish! Ask him to lie back, or if you've been kissing and caressing, gently push him into that position and pull yourself up over him. If it's not already off, help him get his shirt off. Lean over and let the ends of your hair swish back and forth across his chest and abdomen. Keep it out of his face – that's not very sexy! You can alternate this with a fingertip massage before going back to using your hair. Then ask him to turn over on to his stomach and continue stimulating his skin by swishing your hair across his back and even his buttocks.

The Swan Technique

This touching technique will start to build his arousal and anticipation. With the Swan you can give him some initial stimulation of his penis and testicles during foreplay. Think of the swan shape as being formed by your thumb and fingertips, coming together in the shape of a swan's head. One way you can apply this is to clasp his testicles gently between the beak-like shape that is formed by your fingertips. Then use a gentle circular movement and give them a little pull. Relax this small pulling sensation before starting again. Be creative when you clasp his testicles between the 'beak' of your swan-shaped fingertips. His testicles will rest in the palm of your hand while you do this action.

Then you can move your fingertips and swirl them up on to his penis and back down along his inner thighs. This will feel fantastic to him because when you start a certain technique, then take a little break, and then restart it, it teases your lover. And teasing builds desire!

You can also use the Swan technique as an upward movement that starts at the base of his penis. Do this by gripping the base of his penis with your fingertips and the tip of your thumb so that the glans (the head of his penis) is nestled in the palm of your hand. Then pull his foreskin (if he has one) gently up over his glans with your fingertips pulled together. Again you can repeat this and stretch your fingertips and thumb back down around the base of his penis before you gently pull your fingertips upwards.

Footie Heaven

Strangely enough, men have incredibly sensitive feet. You might think they are covered in calluses and would be unresponsive to touch, but actually they're very sensitive, especially around any rough patches. Many massage therapists believe that certain pressure points on the feet extend upwards through 'love lines' to the genitals and beyond. So, by stimulating different points on his feet you'll send pulses of pleasure up through his body.

One sensual pleasure you can offer to do for him is to give him a foot massage – but one with a difference. Just as you love the sensations that a foot massage brings, so will he. First bathe his feet in warm soapy water. Make him feel really spoilt – and the pay-off is that he will be much more likely to spoil you in return. Then take a rich moisturising lotion and massage them slowly and sensually. You'll be surprised, if you take the edge of your forefinger and run it back and forth in the arch of his foot, how much he loves it. Take your time because he may never have experienced the sensations this will give him. Besides doing something sensual for him, a technique like this also stimulates his 'sensitive side', so you are likely to get the same treatment back! And once you've massaged his feet simply run your fingers up his leg and get down to some serious foreplay.

Bottoms Up

Men hold a lot of tension in their upper buttocks. You can help him relax and feel fantastic if you ask him to roll on to his stomach for some massage pleasure. Warm lots of lubricant between your hands and with your thumbs together, just over the cleft of his bottom, lay your palms flat on his buttocks. Then move upwards and outwards, your hands moving away from each other. Continue in a circular movement until your hands meet at his upper cleft. Repeat this sequence slowly and sensuously a few times.

Next, turn your hands slightly upwards with the thumbs on top and swish the outside of your hands upwards over his buttocks. Then turn them over (so that the inside of your fingers and palms touch his skin) and move them back downwards. Repeat this a number of times and vary the sensations you create with the circular movements.

Do the Naughty Dog Kiss on Your Naughty Dog

As I described in Part One, the Naughty Dog Kiss is a very earthy little trick. And men love earthiness! Just to remind you, when doing this kiss, relax your mouth and open it fairly wide as well as relaxing your tongue. Then allow your tongue to make sweeping laps across an erogenous zone.

A perfect place to do this is on his inner thighs. When you two are kissing and caressing each other, move your head down to his hips. You can dive straight down there or plant little kisses along his body as you move. Gently push his legs apart and get between them. Now, open your mouth and find that tender area at the top of his inner thigh, just where it meets his testicles, and begin to lap there. Take your time and build his anticipation between laps. Use big sweeping laps and he'll be gagging for more!

The Pearl Necklace Technique

This is a fantastic little technique that will make him think you're a very experienced lover. When he's lying back and you two have been enjoying foreplay, get out an old beaded necklace – a fake pearl one is ideal. Take his penis between your hands and with lashings of lubricant start moving them up and down.

Next, take your time and carefully wrap the pearl necklace (or any beaded necklace that doesn't have any sharp decorations or a sharp clasp) loosely around the base of his penis. Then, clutch it between one hand and the base of his penis. Place your other hand on top of the hand at the base. Now, start to gently roll the necklace up and down the base of his shaft with the lubricant making it a fluid motion.

This will feel amazing to him! Keep your movements focused on his shaft. Make sure you don't move the necklace so far up his shaft that it catches the base of his glans – his penile head – as that could feel a little painful to him. Also, make sure you don't catch the necklace in his pubic hair.

His Shaven Haven

Women have always had a lot of pressure to remove their pubic hair by shaving, waxing, permanent electrolysis, laser treatments or depilatory creams – either completely or at least partly. Some men are now catching on to the fact that they like to shave or wax their pubic hair, too. They've found they like the feeling of being hair-free.

The great thing about having less hair is that the skin that's revealed from beneath the pubic hair is incredibly sensitive. This is because it's never seen the light of day, so-to-speak. Why not suggest that you shave off some of his pubes and see if he likes it.

If he's game to try it, then have some warm water handy and a sensitive skin-shaving foam. He can sit or lie back on the bed with a big, thick towel underneath him. Make sure you warm his skin up with the warm water, and that you use plenty of the shaving gel or foam, before you begin to shave him. Once you've tidied up his pubic region take some sensitive skin lubricant or aftershave moisture balm and gently rub it into the shaven area. He'll undoubtedly enjoy your gentle touch and being spoilt like this. If he's up for a little bit of sex-play this would be the perfect time to take a vibrator and gently tease this area with the tip of it – up and down and around and around.

Oriental Body Massage

Yes, we are back to 'Eastern ways' for this trick. Men absolutely love the sensation of the softness of a woman's skin against theirs. It contrasts so much with their own skin – which is often hairier and rougher – that it immediately makes them appreciate the difference in the female body. You can heighten his appreciation of your skin by giving him an Oriental Body Massage.

You can do this at any time during foreplay but whenever he's ended up on his back is a good time to begin. Raise yourself up on your arms and allow your naked breasts to gently swish across his chest. Then move downwards so they skim his stomach and hips. Then you can move on top of him in a sort of 'push up' position and glide your entire body, from your hips to your breasts, across his. You can continue to kiss him while you do this or whisper sexy things in his ear while you skim your body in different ways across his. You can also do this massage by asking him to lie on his stomach – again without his clothes on – and skim your naked body across his back and bottom.

Million Dollar Vibrations

You definitely need to know where his 'million-dollar spot' is for this tip. It is located between his legs and at about the centre of his perineum. His perineum is the band of skin that runs from the base of his testicles to his anus. Men may vary in sensitivity at different points on this erogenous zone so you need to find the exact spot that gives him the most pleasure. The million-dollar spot is located over his prostate, so when you stimulate this part of his skin it also puts pressure on his prostate.

Stroke this area with your fingertips and sensually ask him which part of it feels best. Then take a vibrator, using it on low speed, and gently circle his million-dollar spot with it. As always with vibrators, use a lubricant to make it a sexier vibe! Most men love this trick once they've been introduced to it although some may be a little bit inhibited at first by the idea of you using a vibrator in this area. You could also continue stimulating him like this while you lick and suck his penis.

Inner Wrist Magic

'Double-sensory stimulation' has been shown to enhance the foreplay experience. By double-sensory stimulation, I mean using techniques that get two erogenous zones tingling at the same time – this can feel like being in heaven.

One fantastic little trick to do while you're kissing him is to begin stroking his inner wrist. This is an incredible erogenous zone that's definitely neglected in men. As you kiss him, take one of your free hands, reach inside his arm, and start an upward stroking motion from his wrist towards his elbow. Do this really subtly and he'll barely know what's hit him. Magic! He will feel a heightened sense of arousal that he's probably never experienced before.

Sexy Snogs

Turn him on with sizzling kissing! Here are the best possible kissing tips you can learn to make your kisses unforgettable. Obviously, make sure your breath is fresh and if he doesn't like things like spicy food or garlic then avoid these before going to bed with him.

Definitely start slowly and take your time. It's when you rush things that kissing feels stiff or sloppy. Relax and make sure your lips are loosened so they don't feel hard touching his. Start with small, slow and sensual little kisses around his lips. Then let your lips fall open and allow the edge of your tongue to linger in his inner lips. Slightly vary the pressure you use with your tongue and lips. Just planting one kiss on him that doesn't change in pressure or style is very bland and boring. Men really do notice the difference between a good kisser compared to one who isn't.

Stretch It Out

Once you've begun French kissing and you're both enjoying teasing and tantalising each other's tongues, try the Stretch kiss. This is where you allow the tip of your tongue to stretch out and stroke the roof of his mouth.

This is a little known trick that most people never try. But they're missing out because the roof of the mouth is incredibly sensitive. Try for a moment stroking the roof of your own mouth with the tip of your tongue and you'll see what I mean. It's a lovely sensation.

Vary your French kisses and occasionally tantalise the roof of his mouth with the Stretch. A great tip to add into this is another double-sensory stimulation sensation tip. As you stroke the roof of his mouth with the tip of your tongue, use your middle or index finger to stroke the inside of the palm of his hand. He'll love both of these sensations – especially together.

The Very Sexy Vacuum Kiss

Another great kiss to try on him that he will probably never have experienced before is the vacuum kiss. This is a very passionate kiss that feels fantastic. First, you need to relax your lips and then place them around your lover's top or bottom lip. Next use a gentle suction action to gently pull on the outer rim of their lip. You can then momentarily release this pressure on their lips before reapplying.

You might want to focus on either the top or bottom lip before swapping but you can also – depending on the shape of your mouths – encircle both of his lips with yours and apply this gentle vacuum suction.

Think of a vacuum kiss as the basic kiss you'd use on the glans of his penis during oral sex. It's a gentle pulsating action where you release the pressure and then re-apply the pressure, and so on. An extra little tip is to say to him after you've been kissing his lips this way, 'How would you like me to try that on your nob?' Obviously use the word that you two use for the glans of his penis.

Fabulous Fluttering

Get creative with your fingertips and imagine fluttering them gently across your lover's skin. Let them wander over his different erogenous zones from his neck, down and over his chest, around his hips and down his inner thighs. It's so easy to simply flutter your fingertips across him like this while you're kissing.

As you two are getting more turned on, use this fluttering all over his testicles – very gently at first but then you can ask him if you can build up the pressure. Because most women simply stroke a man's testicles he'll respond fantastically to this fluttering sensation across them. You can also try fluttering behind his knees while you are giving him oral sex.

The Gratifying Grip

You could surprise him with this little trick that both turns him on and also makes him wonder what will happen next. As you're kissing and caressing each other simply reach your hand around the base of the shaft of his penis, grip the base, and keep your hand perfectly still. The rest of you will be active – your lips, your body, even your other hand, but this hand around the base of his penis will remain completely still.

What happens is that this trick builds his desire for you to move the still hand because it teases him. As soon as he starts moving his hips a little you'll know he's getting very excited because he's showing you that he wants you to start moving your hand. But instead, you're going to be a naughty little vixen and continue to just hold his erection firmly with the Grip until he begs you to start moving your hand. It's up to you how soon you start giving him the hand action he wants!

Boost His Sense of Masculinity

This is one of the simplest touching techniques you could ever try. The subtle message you give to him is what a 'masculine' man he is. Men will often privately say things like they wish the woman in their life would make them feel more manly. This trick will help you do so.

As you're kissing him, or nuzzling and caressing him, allow your hand to move up to one of his biceps. The bicep is the long muscle at the front of his arm, running from the shoulder down towards his elbow. Even if your man is slim or lanky you can still take your hand, and using long caressing strokes, move it from his shoulder down to his elbow. You might also like to use some lubricant and run your hand up and down his bicep.

You will boost his sense of masculinity if you do this through foreplay because he'll get the subtle message that you can't resist touching his big muscles – even if they're weedy little ones! The pay-off for you is that once he's feeling very 'manly', it will boost his sexual confidence to do more pleasurable and sexy things to you.

Lasting Longer

Many men are worried about lasting long enough during penetrative sex or even during foreplay. If they're getting really turned on, they start to worry that they'll climax before you're anywhere near ready. But, if you think this may happen, you can use this trick very subtly so he won't feel that you're complaining.

Tell him how good it feels to pulsate his PC muscle – those are the pelvic-floor muscles that run from his pubic bone around to his anus. (Women also have pelvic-floor muscles.) When he's nice and erect during foreplay suggest that he pulsates these muscles. You can tell him that you've been told it strengthens the erection, leading to a better orgasm once it's time to climax. It does do this too, but crucially, what it also does is teach him to last longer. When you actually get down to full sex ask him to do the pulsations again, and not only will you feel them inside you, but they will slow him down from reaching orgasm too quickly.

Randy Restraints

Somehow, many people buy into the myth that it's practically always the man who restrains his female partner in a bit of bondage-play. This couldn't be further from the truth! Many men love the sensation of being a little restrained.

A little trick to give him a taste of bondage-play is simply to restrain his hands with handcuffs or, if you don't have any, by tying them with a dressing-gown sash or even one of his neckties. Have a lovely lubricant to hand and after warming it between the palms of your hands, swish them back and forth across his chest and then move down to his pelvic region. This is the perfect time for a little bit of dirty talk where you tell him all the things you'd like to do to him with his hands bound together.

Vary Those Vibrations

The fantastic thing about vibrators (and there'll be more on sex toys to come) is that they can be used in all sorts of ways. Now that you've tried using a vibrator on his million-dollar spot, why not ask him to turn on to his stomach during foreplay. Move across so that you're sitting lightly on his thighs. Then take some lubricant and smooth it over his bottom and begin to use the vibrator to circle his buttocks.

Now, slowly trace a line up the crack of his bottom to the cleft at the top. Start a figure-of-eight action where you move the vibrator's tip around one buttock, arriving back at his crack, then moving up to the cleft, and then circle his other buttock. Repeat this figure of eight as many times as you want.

Next you can move the vibrator down and simply hold it gently where his upper thighs meet his buttocks. That sensation will go through to his million-dollar spot. After you've been holding it there for a while, you can start nudging the vibrator into little circular actions. You'll probably want to continue with other foreplay but find that he wants you to continue stimulating him with a vibrator in this way!

Sextion Two

Tips for Delicious Oral Sex
for His Pleasure

One of the biggest complaints men make is that they don't get enough oral sex. But, quite frankly, tons of oral sex would never be enough in most men's books! However, if you really want to wrap him around your little finger in bed – and out of it – try some of these oral sex techniques that will leave him super-satisfied.

Tongue Magic

People forget that the tongue is a muscle – and like any other muscle it needs to be kept in shape! To give the most mind-blowing oral pleasure, your tongue should be ready for action.

Here are a few tips to get it ready for oral sex. Firstly, allow your mouth to fall open and your tongue to hang loose. Now flick the tip of it up and down so that it taps your upper lip. Secondly, with your mouth open circle your tongue around and around and then swap directions and circle it the other way. You'll be surprised how one direction is easier than the other – and you need it to be flexible in all directions. Thirdly, open your lips so your tongue can slip out between them, then move it back and forth rubbing your lips as you go.

You'll probably be amazed how you get tongue-fatigue with these little exercises. That means you have a lazy tongue and you need to get it in better shape to give the best possible oral sex!

Handle With Care

You might think that if a man has a foreskin he won't be overly sensitive but until you know him well you need to treat his foreskin with care. Just as you may not want your clitoral hood pulled back either unexpectedly or even when he's been stroking it, too quickly, a man with a foreskin will feel the same way.

What you can do as you touch his foreskin is ask him if he likes it moved up and down during oral pleasure. Or maybe he prefers to have it pulled back completely and held in place while you kiss, lick or suck him. One little trick with his foreskin that will help desensitise it temporarily, is to take a blob of lubricant on your index finger and simply run it around and around the base of his foreskin. Then, when you pull back his foreskin – ever so gently – continue with another blob of lubricant to run around and around the edge/base of his glans. This may just blow his mind!

You also need to treat his frenulum with care. The frenulum is the ligament on the underside of his glans that holds the foreskin in place and it is very sensitive.

Tongue Fluttering

A sizzling tip to try (and your tongue should be ready for this type of action after a few tongue exercises) is to use your tongue in a fluttering way; the way you imagine a butterfly's wings move. Quickly, and gently, flutter your tongue up and down and around the base of his glans and then up to the tip of his penis. Alternate fluttering around the base with some fluttering upwards to the tip of his penis. Then create a new sensation by holding all of his glans in your mouth and applying a gentle suction before going back to the fluttering action. He'll love this alternating sensation of suction and fluttering.

Sensual Shaft Treatment

Like women, men differ tremendously in how much pressure they like applied to their different erogenous zones. This is, of course, true with the shaft of his penis. Some men will want you to get hold of it, and hold it as you do all the various oral sex techniques you know to his glans. Others will like their shaft stimulated continually with an up and down movement. And, of course, some men will want their shaft teased, tickled and stroked in the same way you might treat the glans of his penis.

Unless he really likes one of these over and above the others, you can mix these tricks up and treat his shaft like a 'mission of discovery'! So, begin by holding it fairly firmly as you use some sort of tonguing technique on his glans – like the fluttering technique just mentioned. Then you can try moving your hand up and down on his shaft in small strokes. And next, alternate between these two. He'll love it if you look up at him, while going down on his penis, and ask him what feels best and what he'd like more of.

The Lollipop Lick

Although men will play with their testicles when they play with their penis, many have never had a woman do so. That means they may worry about asking a woman to stimulate their testicles.

As with doing any oral sex, you always want someone to be fresh and clean.

What you can do to start stimulating his testicles is the Lollipop Lick. Imagine you're holding a lollipop in front of your face and you're lapping at it with your extended tongue. That's the action you want to get!

When, during foreplay, you've moved down towards his abdomen and hips you can then nudge his legs apart and start lapping at his testicles. A good trick is to cup them with one hand as you kneel over his lower legs supporting yourself with your other hand. Ever so slightly, pull them away from his body with your cupped hand and lap at them as if you're lapping at some juicy plums in the palm of your cupped hand.

Humming is Never Humdrum

This is a great, fun, and sometimes funny, technique! Think about how the inside of your mouth vibrates when you hum a tune. Now think about applying that to your lover's testicles or the end of his penis. Hold his penis in your mouth (or his testicles, one at a time) and hum quietly to yourself. He'll love the natural vibrations you give him.

The best way to do this is to pause when you've been licking or kissing him in one way or another, and then apply the humming technique. Of course many people don't want to make what they might think of as a silly noise during sex, but the lovely gentle sensations you'll create will mean he won't be thinking about your humming. If he does, there's nothing wrong with having a laugh about humming a tune on his testicles!

Luscious Licking

There's licking and then there's luscious licking. Your tongue should now be ready for luscious licking if you've been doing my tongue exercises each day! Begin with a little 'sexy spit and polish': dip your fingertips into your mouth and collect a little saliva on to them from your tongue. Rub that over the end of his penis to pre-moisten it. Then slip your fully wet mouth over the end of his penis.

Swirl your tongue around and around the head of his penis. Now remove his head from your mouth and lick him from the base of his shaft right up to the tip of his glans as if he's a lovely ice lolly! Slip your tongue up and down with lots of luscious licks.

Remove your mouth and slip some more saliva on to your fingertips and begin to stimulate his glans again with that. Make sure he's watching you do it and that you do it in a very erotic way as you dip your fingertips into your mouth.

Naughty Kneeling

Ideally, it's best to do this when you're having sex-play in bed but you can also do it on a carpeted floor. Lying on your back, suggest that he kneels above your chest with his legs apart. You can reach up and hold his testicles with your hands while he tilts his penis into your mouth. He can lightly swirl his penis around inside your mouth while you lick and suck it. Then you can pull him out of your mouth, as the kneeling position gives you fantastic access to his testicles, and you can lap and lick these or even hold one in your mouth while you play with his penis with your other hand.

This is also a great position for you to reach around and hold his bottom with your hands as he guides his penis in and out of your mouth.

Sexy Suction

As the man gets increasingly aroused, he often likes a suction action to be applied with your mouth and lips. Always check with him how hard or gentle he wants such a suction to be. He can slide the whole of his glans into your mouth and you can form a suction around it with your lips. Then you can help him glide in and out of your lips – your lips will 'catch' gently as they move back and forth over the edge of his glans. He'll probably want his foreskin pulled back during this.

He'll love the suction feeling around the edge of his glans. As you get more skilled you can give him a little tongue action while you keep your lips suctioned around his glans. Simply flicker your tongue around the end of his penis while you maintain the suction for a fantastic feeling.

Worship at His Altar

Here is an incredibly hot technique to use with him. All you have to do is kneel between his legs while he stands above you. From this position you can reach up and hold his hips while you give him oral sex. Or, if he likes his bottom caressed, you can reach between his thighs and stroke his buttocks for extra stimulation.

This position is fantastic for a little bit of fantasy play where he's your master and you're his sex slave. You can look up at him and ask him what his bidding is. Ask him to hold the back of your head while you're between his legs and to guide your movements while his penis is in your mouth.

Ice, Ice Baby

For a little bit of a thrill – particularly in warmer weather – suck on an ice cube before you take him in your mouth. You can keep a tumbler full of ice cubes on the bedside table or on the coffee table if you're giving him oral sex in your sitting room.

The first time you go to lick him with your ice-cool mouth he may have a bit of a surprise, but as your mouth warms up, and you suck another ice cube, you'll find he loves the varying temperature of your mouth. If he's feeling daring you can take the ice cube between your lips and move it around his testicles and between his legs and across his inner thighs. Then, remove the ice cube and as your tongue warms up you can lick these areas to warm them back up.

Picking the Plums

This is an interesting technique to try that will give him slightly different sensations. Imagine him kneeling on the bed, resting back on his legs. This leaves his penis and testicles hanging free for you to play with. He might be kneeling after he slips out of his clothes and is getting into bed. Instead of letting him do this, you can nestle your head between his knees and arch your head up to reach his testicles and penis with your mouth. Your hands are also free to touch and tease him as you give him oral pleasure. The fantastic twist on this position is he simply needs to reach down and he can fondle your breasts while you're licking and sucking him.

Fondle Me, Too

This is another little trick that will give you pleasure at the same time as you're giving him oral pleasure. And there's nothing wrong with you getting enjoyment too – in fact there's everything right about it!

Imagine he's lying back on the bed and you're going to give him oral sex. Move your head down to his hips and start caressing him and sucking him. But shift your own hips round, towards his upper body, so that they're at a right angle to his body. This way he can fondle you while you suck and kiss him. Not only do you get some stimulation but he'll be doubly aroused by touching you while you stimulate him with your mouth.

Minty Mouth

You can give your lover a whole new sensation by first sucking a mint in your mouth before giving him oral sex. When you take his penis in your mouth he'll get extra stimulation from the minty-ness of your mouth. They put menthol in some of the topical (that means applied to the skin) 'aphrodisiacs' and this gently excites the skin as it will do when you suck him after eating a mint.

He will get the same sensation if you hold some toothpaste in your mouth before sucking him. Or you can try this with a low-strength mouthwash. Just make sure he's not an extra sensitive man as this might be a little bit too much stimulation!

The Juicer

Here's a trick to do with your hands while you're giving him oral sex. Remember a key tip during any sexual technique is to pause for a moment to do something else to arouse your lover and then go back to whatever you were doing first. You can do this after you've been sucking him for while – and then go back to sucking him.

Be careful not to put too much pressure on his penis when doing this technique. First, hold the base of his shaft with one hand while your other hand holds his glans in the palm of your hand as if you're about to start juicing an orange. Begin by rotating one hand back and forth very gently and then add in the other hand. Lashings of lubricant will make your hands slip fantastically on him. Because you'll be stimulating both ends of his penis – the glans and the base of the shaft – continue to ask him to guide you as to how fast you should do the turning movements with your hands and also what sort of pressure is right for him.

More Good Vibrations

You can get him to help you out during this technique. As you're kissing and sucking his penis, spread lashings of lubricant on the area of his perineum. Then have him hold the shaft of his penis while you continue sucking the glans and use a vibrator on his perineum. He'll find it fairly mind-blowing to have the vibrating sensations going through his skin and stimulating his prostate while you're sucking the head of his penis. Experiment a little and ask him to take control of the vibrator while you go back to using your hand to massage his shaft. Notice what he does with the vibrator between his legs. Maybe he'll stimulate his testicles with it, or focus on his perineum, or run it around his inner thighs. By seeing what he likes to do, when you take control of the vibrator again you can do the things you now know he loves best.

Shower Sucking

You and he can get up to all sorts of sudsy, sexy fun in the shower. This technique is a fantastic one to surprise him with. Make sure you've got a nice, thick face cloth or even a hand towel rolled up to kneel on. Enjoy sharing a shower with him, soaping each other down in a sexy way (a little tip – be careful which type of soaps or shower gels you use on your genitals because they can upset the delicate ph balance and irritate, rather than clean, the genitals). Then, place the hand towel or face cloth under your knees while you go down between his legs as in Worship at His Altar as previously mentioned. From here you can give him some oral pleasure (you might save giving him a blow-job for once you're out of the shower) with the shower cascading around you.

The top practical tip to make this successful is to ask him to angle the showerhead so it hits his back – and runs down his back – and doesn't swamp you with water as you kneel in front of him.

Changing the 'Guard'

Here is one of the easiest tips in my book – but one that will give him quite a bit of added pleasure. Depending on what 'handedness' you are – either right- or left-handed – you probably tend to use that hand to stimulate his shaft while you kiss and lick his glans. But to give him a new sensation, after a couple of minutes of rhythmically stimulating his shaft, shift to your other hand. It will feel quite different because you won't be used to using that hand. For added fun, tell him he can fantasise that this other hand is the hand of another woman! You can then alternate between your hands every minute or so, changing the sensations as he gets into this incredibly easy technique.

Tastes So Sweet

This is a very sexy trick to use on him. Once you've been giving him some oral sex for a few minutes, slip him out of your mouth, and mount him so that he can slip inside your vagina. Allow him to do a couple of thrusts before you get off of him and then return to licking your own juices from his penis.

Men find this a huge turn-on! Don't turn your nose up before you try it – after all you expect him to give you oral pleasure so you shouldn't worry about tasting a little bit of your own juices off of him. You can then alternate between sucking him off, mounting him for a bit and then licking him again.

Other Oral Sensations

You can take all sorts of things into your mouth to give him other oral sensations. If you two have opened a bottle of bubbly then take a sip from the fizzy champagne and immediately take him into your mouth so he enjoys the fizzing bubbles on his glans. Or, take a bowl of ice cream to bed, spoon-feed each other, and then chill down your mouth with a spoonful before he places his penis in your mouth. You can melt a piece of chocolate in your mouth – or take a bite of chocolate mousse – before slipping him into your mouth so he can feel the smooth and creamy sensations on his penis. Or, lick a teaspoon of sticky honey before sucking him for a different, sticky sensation. You can also sip a hot drink to make your mouth super warm before he slips in.

Deep Throating

If men have seen a lot of porn films most of them assume that they're going to find 'deep throating' the ultimate oral sex experience. However, due to the natural gag reflex, most women can't do deep throating and they don't like the choking sensation when they try. But there's nothing wrong with a little bit of sex-perimentation and even if it doesn't work out, he can fantasise about your attempts to take all of him into your mouth.

The important thing is that you need to be in a position where your throat lines up with your mouth – so that means your head tilted fairly far back. You can get into this position by tucking some pillows right under your neck so the top of your head can rest back, touching the mattress. Lie comfortably in the centre of your bed with your upper back and head well propped like this. He can kneel above you and try sliding his penis in as far as you find comfortable.

Another position you can try is to lie sideways across a big easy chair so that your head and neck rest over the edge of it – again allowing your mouth and throat to line up. He can stand by the side of the armchair and try and ease himself in – usually he has to bend his knees to do so. You could also kneel between his legs on some cushions to raise you up. You drop your head well back as long as he supports the back of your head with his two hands – and you might find this position helps him get further in. Whatever you do don't try practising with something like a carrot or a banana – you could choke to death!

Sextion Three

Tips to Liven Up Sex Positions for Him

Men, of course, love having sex but often feel they have to take charge of initiating different sexual positions. Make sure you initiate new sex positions when you think about them to take the pressure off of him.

Men also feel they have to keep quite focused on keeping their thrusting going so their partner gets sexual fulfilment. Let him know that it's absolutely fine to vary the pressure and speed of his thrusting. Reassure him that you'll tell him (in the nicest and most sensual way of course) if it disrupts the stimulation you need to reach orgasm. By using these little tips, tricks and techniques, in the positions suggested, you can give him much more enjoyment during actual penetration. Of course, many of these tips can also be used with different positions, so be creative.

Stirred Not Shaken

Women often make the 'mistake' of allowing the man to do all the movement during thrusting, but you can create really sensual sensations by simply moving your hips slightly in a round-and-round 'stirring' action as he thrusts. This is particularly good during slow and sensual sex.

It's best to practise moving your hips around in small, circular motions when you're standing in the shower and imagining having sex with him. Think of it as a 'stirring' movement. You can get a little rhythm going, but remember it's a small movement you want, not a big circular one the way a lap dancer moves her hips. This is perfect when he's behind you, say, in the Spoons position or even Doggy style. As long as he's holding you and thrusting back and forth you can gently do this action to heighten both of your sensations.

Stand and Deliver 'Added Extra'

There's something very exciting about standing positions – they feel so wanton and abandoned. In Stand and Deliver you, of course, get support from leaning against a wall while he enters you – and you're facing each other. But this position gives you the perfect chance to give him a little added extra stimulation by fondling his buttocks. As well as giving you something to hold on to, it will feel fantastic to him. Think of each of your hands 'kneading', or rhythmically clenching in-and-out, one buttock each as he gets in the rhythm of thrusting, and that's the movement you want to achieve.

Hog Tied

For a little bit of naughty pleasure for him – and this is particularly good for men who have a penis on the smaller size – volunteer to be 'hog tied' during penetration. By this I simply mean having your ankles tied together to give him more stimulation. Anything that's soft and won't hurt you, and that comes to hand easily will be great to use. You could use one of his neckties or the sash from a dressing gown.

Imagine you're in bed together and you can sexily suggest that you or he gently ties your ankles together. He can then enter you from behind in Spoons position, or you can slip over on top of him. Having your ankles being tied will give an added tension and friction to the thrusting.

The Puppet 'Plus'

This is a great but under-used position. In the Puppet he's behind you, you're both standing up, and you relax forward, either leaning your hands on a sofa or the edge of the bed, or dangling towards the floor. This is great for a 'bum man' who loves bottoms!

Here's a naughty little tip to enhance his pleasure during the Puppet. Hand him a vibrator and as he's sensually and slowly thrusting in and out of you, ask him to stimulate your bottom with it. He can circle it around and around your cheeks and then slowly trace a line from the cleft of your bottom down your crack. Really push your hips upwards towards him so that he has the time of his life enjoying your beautiful bottom!

The Staging Post 'Pull'

Always a great position when passion has overtaken you and you end up moving from, say, having started your romp in bed, to wanting to move to the floor or vice versa. A quick reminder that the woman is kneeling with one or both legs on the end of the bed or with one foot resting on the floor. He's behind her with his feet on the floor and holding on to her hips so that he can thrust.

This is a perfect position for the woman to reach between her legs, back behind her, and to take hold of his testicles lightly. Every time he thrusts apply a very gentle squeeze and pull to his testicles to enhance his pleasure.

The 'Sexed-Up' Straddle

With him sitting on the edge of a bed or sofa, and you straddling his lap, knees either side of his hips and facing him, this is a perfect position for a little trick with partial penetration. Partial penetration is one way of him teasing you during thrusting. He uses partial penetration to heighten your sexual excitement before he allows full thrusting to take place.

What you can do is raise yourself up so that just the head of his penis is inside you. You can either use small up-and-down movements so the head of his penis pulls in and out of your vaginal lips. Or you can drive him crazy by doing the little circular movements as described in Stirred Not Shaken earlier. This partial penetration, using these two techniques, will drive both of you crazy and you'll be dying to get back to full thrusting.

The Rocking-Chair Manoeuvre

If he happens to be a little bit of an 'earthy' guy who loves touching his lover's clitoris then he'll like this little trick. The Rocking Chair isn't a position for someone who doesn't have much strength. He kneels on the ground, or on the bed (if the mattress is firm), and she has her back towards him and slips her bottom on to his lap with her knees bent. This is a lovely, sensual position that takes quite a bit of strength as he thrusts, moving up and down – even doing small movements takes some strength. Alternatively, you can do the moving up and down on him.

But there are lots of little tricks you can do in this position. He'll love it if you ask him to take complete control of your pleasure and pull one of his hands around your hips to your clitoris. Then, showing him the pressure with which he should either circle that area or hold it as you to move, you can then let him stimulate you. Or, you can reach between your legs and rub the base of his shaft with small back and forth movements as he thrusts in and out. Also, you could give him a vibrator and ask him to reach around with it to stimulate your clitoral region – or you could use a vibrator on both of you as you two enjoy this sexy position. These added techniques will super-charge your pleasure!

Easy Over Ecstasy

In this position the man really gets to feel in control. It's a great one for spontaneous passion when in your sitting room. The woman (who needs to be flexible) slips down her panties and trousers or skirt, moves behind a sturdy armchair or sofa and sits on the back. He clasps her hands and then lets her lie back slowly so that her head and shoulders can rest on the seat of the chair or sofa. This means she's arched over the comfortable back of the seat.

If he's quite kinky he'll love this little tip – while he thrusts slowly she should ask him to massage her pubic mound. She's so exposed to him in this position (with her pelvis perched on the back of the sofa and seeing her as she's arched back) that he'll get a complete thrill! The trick is to take his hand and guide it to the pubic mound and ask him to make circular massage motions in rhythm with his thrusting, in and out. It's hard to know who gets more benefit from this technique – her, because it will feel fantastic, or him, because he gets a full view of arousing her!

Kinky Kitchen Counter

It's no secret that men love a bit of 'kinky-lite' as I call it. And the more spontaneous it is, the better. However, you can pretend that this is spontaneous but actually have thought it through. The only thing you need to prepare is having a couple cushions to hand to pad out your bottom or his knees. When you two are sharing dinner or cooking at the kitchen counter why not suggest that he takes you on the kitchen counter. It's actually easier and more comfortable to do than you'd imagine!

You can slip out of your skirt or trousers and simply bend over the counter while he takes you from behind. You could also bend over the tabletop. If your table has sturdy legs, then flirt with him and tease him into taking you on the tabletop. You don't even have to go all the way with a bit of Kinky Kitchen action. You could hop up on the kitchen counter, if it's strong enough, having taken your knickers off, and suggest he gets down on his knees and gives you oral sex then and there. Men love a bit of domination in the kitchen!

Desk Delight

While we're on the subject of sexy tricks that get you out of the bedroom and into interesting sex with him elsewhere, why not visit him after hours at his work and begin foreplay there. With your bottom propped against the edge of his desk, he can take you in the Stand and Deliver position as described earlier. Or you can do The Wrap, where you sit on the edge of his desk, with him between your legs, but his feet on the floor. You wrap your legs around his waist. He needs to thrust slowly in this position so that he doesn't come out of you but it can give deep and satisfying penetration!

Of course you can seduce him in these positions on the desk in your own office or at home if you have a desk there. Why not kick off with a bit of fantasy chat? Make a couple of suggestive remarks about what the boss 'needs' and that you're happy to provide it.

The 'Added' Twist

Use the Twist position for a sexy little way to flaunt your breasts for his pleasure. In the Twist position the woman is lying on her back but propped up on her elbows. The man is on his side with one arm propping him up on his elbow and the other arm wrapped around her waist or chest. He inter-links his legs with hers.

Once in this position it requires slow and sensual thrusting. The woman can throw her head back pushing out her breasts – a huge sexual stimulus for him. He can also lean down to kiss her breasts in this position. A great tip for the man who's on the smaller size is that this position gives fantastic friction.

Unfold the Flower

Unfold the Flower is a sensational position for the supple woman. It gives him deep penetration and you can look into each other's eyes for greater intimacy. You lie on your back and get him to pull your legs up on to his shoulders so that your knees rest on them. He is now in a kneeling position between your legs. As well as your flexibility, it requires some strength on his part but the deep access it gives makes it worth it!

A little trick you can do to give him extra pleasure is to reach around underneath your bottom, holding a vibrator, and push it upwards gently to tickle the base of his shaft and testicles during thrusting. This added stimulation can get him very excited so you may want to do it for a minute or two then remove the vibrator from his genitals and then restart again when he has regained control.

Magic Muscles

One of the easiest tricks you can use in practically any sex position is to make your vaginal muscles work to give him pleasure! What you need to do is tighten and release them in a rhythmic fashion. It's best during slower thrusting so that he can feel the tension and relaxation of them. As you build up the strength of these muscles you can try pulsating them at a quicker rhythm. That will really turn him on.

'Extra' Sexy Spoons

The Spoons is a lovely, relaxed position where the couple is lying on their sides, the man behind the woman. The first trick you can use during the Spoons, to give him added pleasure, is to move your upper leg – by 'upper' I mean if the woman is lying on her right side the upper leg is her left leg. By moving it upwards, slightly backwards or slightly forwards, or by bending your knee in various ways, the movement places more or less pressure on his penis inside you.

The next tip in the Spoons position is to reach between your legs and gently take hold of his testicles. You can massage these with care during slower thrusting. This will definitely enhance his orgasm!

The 'Delicious' Double Header

For the man in your life who loves your breasts, here's a little tip to have fun with. The Delicious Double Header is not an active position but one for slow and sensual movements. It's called the

Double Header because when in position his head is behind yours – imagine his chin touching the back of your shoulder.

He's sitting on the floor, or on the bed with his back against the bedhead or wall (or if on the floor, with his back against the sofa). You sit in his lap, legs outside of his. By bending your knees and pushing from the floor, while he holds your hips, you can do small movements up and down on his penis. But the tip is to slip one of his hands around to fondle your breasts while you take a break from the thrusting action. Also this is a perfect position for you to reach between your legs and hold on to his testicles while you two continue to make small movements.

The Resting Dog 'Reach'

As already mentioned earlier in the book, the Resting Dog is perfect for the man who enjoys his lover's bottom. This is where she has slipped down on to her elbows from classic Doggy position where she would be upright on all fours on her hands and knees. When she slips down into the Resting Dog it lifts her pelvis high so that he gets a perfect view of her bottom.

However, for his added pleasure in this position you can reach between your legs with one hand, find his testicles, and stroke them as his excitement builds or gently 'slap' them. You can also wriggle in a side-to-side movement during slower thrusting to give both of you a new sensation.

The Squeeze Technique

This technique can be applied for his pleasure when you're in any position with your legs between his – like the variation of the Reverse Missionary position or the variation of the Clitoral

Alignment Technique (CAT) when your legs are inside his rather than his inside yours.

Once in position all you have to do is cross your ankles and start squeezing your inner thighs. With a little practice, you can reach a point where you can pulsate your thighs as you squeeze them together. Some women find it heightens their own orgasm but certainly it drives some men crazy!

Girls on Top 'Tease'

Get playful in this position and build up his anticipation by 'teasing' him. He lies down in this position on his back and you sit astride him, knees bent and the lower half of your legs resting on the bed. This gives you leverage to lift up and down. He holds your hips to help you move.

However, the trick is that after, say, a dozen up-and-down movements, you pull away from him so that his penis slips out of you. But then you reach down and hold his penis and continue stimulating him with your hand. You then let go and slip him back inside you and begin to move up and down on his penis again before pulling away and re-stimulating him with your hand. The two very different sensations really tease him and build his desire.

Split the Whisker

This is a position where the man crouches on his knees as the woman lies on her back. She rests one leg on his shoulder. He then holds her hips, thighs or knees in order to keep control of them and to avoid slipping out of her. This position can be done either in bed or on the floor as long as he can crouch comfortably.

Men find this an exciting position as they have a view of their lover's vagina. Because you are essentially lying on your back, what you can do is give him a unique sensation by rubbing back and forth over his pubic bone with your fingertips. When he's erect and inside you, this pubic zone is easily reached. You simply use your fingertips in a back and forth movement or you can do small circular motions. Another little tip is that you can also then start stimulating yourself by circling your clitoral region – something he will love to watch!

Missionary Magic

This is a unique little technique to try when in the Missionary position. Of course, he is on top and you have your legs open so he's between them. What you need to do to give him a unique sensation is to form two fists with your hands and reach around to the centre of each of his buttocks. If you imagine an action as if you're kneading dough, this is what you do to the centre of each buttock. If it's done too hard, it can be painful but if it's done too softly it can tickle him. You need to aim for small circular kneading motions with the knuckles of your hands in the centre of each buttock. Because this trick releases tension in the buttocks it gives him a powerful sensation during sex.

Lubed-up Condoms

If you're using condoms, then this little tip will maximise his pleasure. All you have to do is squeeze a drop of a condom-friendly lubricant inside the tip of the condom before he slips it on. That little drop of lubricant will slide around his glans and give him the sensation that's more like feeling a woman's moist vagina.

Sextion Four

Tips for Enhancing His Sexual Fantasies

You may not want to know what goes on in the dark recesses of men's sexual fantasies but believe me they can be naughty boys. By playing to his fantasy life with the following tips, tricks and techniques you may end up reaping the rewards of his sexual excitement! Here are some tips to try and some classic fantasies that are bound to turn him on.

Phone Fantasy

There's nothing like receiving a call from your girlfriend, partner or wife where suddenly she starts a fantasy conversation. Men love a little spontaneous fantasy chat! Why not ring him up and pretend to be 'the mistress of his dreams'. The more detail you go in to – I'm talking loads of delicious detail! – the more turned on he'll get.

You'd be surprised how he'll respond to such a spontaneous fantasy phone call. If you're in a new relationship he'll think he's struck gold and if you've been together for a while, it's a fantastic way of kick-starting a new phase in your sex life.

Naughty Nurse

For all the 'front' men tend to have, where they act as if they want to be in charge and in control, you'll find in lots of their fantasy life they're not in control but are being 'looked after' in some shape or form. One of the sexiest and simplest fantasies to play out panders to this – where you become a naughty nurse.

You can create this in a fairly subtle way. Let's say he's lying back and relaxing on the bed or sofa. What you can do is come up to him, kneel down beside him and start stroking his forehead. You can then tell him that you're a 'naughty nurse' and you're going to give him a very special and sexy examination. Play up the idea of naughtiness and also the fact that you'll be in charge of sorting out his 'problems'. Play with ideas like taking his temperature and doing 'procedures' on him. Allowing him to feel that he's in good hands and can 'let go' is a lovely technique for tapping into another side to his character and sexuality. The trick of this dynamic, where you are in control, can be played out in many ways: you're the college lecturer and he's the student who hasn't done his essay; you're the head of personnel and he's been sent to you because of transgressions on the job; you're the airline stewardess and he's the tipsy passenger you have to sort out. I'm sure you get the picture!

Identity Swap

This tip is all about creating a new look. Men are such visual creatures that it's worthwhile playing around with the way you look and surprising them. We always think men are so bad about noticing what we're wearing or how we've styled our hair but even if they don't comment on it, at a subtle level they are affected by changes in our appearance. And that effect is often to do with sexual attraction.

If you don't live together ask him to come over. Or, if you do live together plan this for when he gets home. Surprise him by greeting him at the door wearing a wig that gives you a completely different look. Take the fantasy play one step further by telling him your name is 'Veronica' – anything but your own name, of course! Have little fun flirting with him looking like a different woman. This is practically a guarantee of some sizzling sex!

Innocent Exposure

There's nothing like playing the 'innocent' and doing something a bit naughty to kick-start a fantasy scenario. A great little tip is to simply bend over for him when wearing a short skirt with only skimpy knickers on or even no knickers, and pretend you don't realise you're flashing him. Keep the pretence up, acting all innocent, to allow him a good look up your skirt.

I know many women will be thinking, 'Oh, I'm too overweight to do that!' but you're missing the point. He will *not* be noticing your weight as you bend down to tidy up CDs while going commando – and while he's slyly trying to look up your skirt!

Another alternative is to sit down wearing a really short skirt and sexy, or no, knickers underneath. Let your skirt ride up and pretend not to notice as you sit next to him. You can then do a real 'Carry On' type of moment where you pretend to catch him out and pull him up for having a naughty peek up your skirt. This is a fantastic way to inspire some fantasy chat.

Sizzling Sex Slave

Simulating fantasy role play is always a great thing for keeping your sex life lively. A fantastic way of doing this is to play Sizzling Sex Slave with each other. Treat this as a special event and mark it out as one day or night in your diary. Be inventive in deciding who plays the sex slave and who plays the master. You could flip a coin or play a game to decide who plays which role.

Once the slave has been designated and the date is in the diary, make sure that nothing interferes with your naughty pleasure. It's the slave's responsibility to pick up some interesting sex toys, clothing, rude food, music etc. – anything necessary to set the scene before the date. When it comes time to enjoy your afternoon or evening, you should remind yourself that you deserve this time together, and you don't want any interruptions – so turn off your mobiles and focus solely on each other. The sex slave can begin by running the master a bath, and they can do things like massaging the master's shoulders as they luxuriate in the sudsy water. The slave can pour a drink and help them sip it. All the master's needs are attended to. The slave can towel them off when they get out of the bath, and then the master gets to choose what they do first. Maybe the master wants to tease the slave by caressing and stroking them while they lie on the bed. Or the master might want to go straight into having sex in a position of their choice. The slave should allow the master to take the lead, and hopefully both of you will enjoy the freedom this role-play gives you. Remember, next time round – maybe in a month or so – you get to swap roles.

Get Dirty

Women are always telling their men to clean up – when they've been in the garden, when they've been tinkering on their car, or when they've been doing DIY. However, this fantasy tip does the exact opposite. Suggest that he puts on some grubby jeans because you have a 'dirty job' for him to do. Then you turn it into fantasy play where he's a repairman that's come to fix your washing machine. You're the posh lady of the house and you can't resist this bit of rough. Have fun getting down and dirty with him!

The Cheeky Boss

This tip reverses the tables from Naughty Nurses and allows him to be in charge. Suggest to him that he'll be the boss and you've come for an interview. During the interview you start being flirty with each other and then you both realise that there is hot sexual chemistry between you.

He becomes the cheeky boss that describes the 'extras' to the job and then suggests you have to do some sexy things if you want to pass the interview. This dynamic – where he's in control – works equally well with many themes: if he pretends to be a police detective and you're the suspect; he's the driving instructor and you're the trainee driver; he's the conductor on the train and when he asks you for your ticket, you've failed to buy one, and so on!

Fantasy Must Dos

Here are some general tips to make sure your fantasy play with him goes well. We may not give them much credit, but some men are very sensitive to new suggestions and if you want to broaden your sexual repertoire and include fantasy chat and scenarios you need to handle things with care. Always use a sensual tone of voice when suggesting a fantasy. Unless it's part of the fantasy (as in role-playing a dominatrix), using a bossy, sarcastic or snide tone with him as in, 'You're not going to be any good at this, but do you think you can pretend to be a sexy builder who has arrived at my home?' will not turn him on!

Although spontaneous fantasy play is fantastic, if you've had a fantasy scenario on your mind then get together the items you might need to play it out beforehand. Never make a fantasy scenario threatening and always let him know that these are just suggestions, and that you have loads more, so if a particular fantasy you've raised turns him off you don't have to do it. If you and he are enjoying your fantasy chat then some fantasies can easily turn into full role play. For example, it's quite easy to role-play Strangers in the Night and meet up at a random bar pretending not to know each other. You then go on to pick each other up for a 'one-night stand' of no-strings sex. Or, you might want to pretend to be the lustful librarian and the only prop you need is some little specs to prop on the end of your nose to make you look like a librarian. But other fantasy scenarios take much more in terms of costume and location.

Naughty Nicknames

A fun little tip to spice up your fantasy chat is to give each other fantasy nicknames. They can be as sexy, fun or dirty as you like! You might choose to call him the Masked Raider if your fantasy is about him being a gorgeous stranger who swoops into your window in the middle of the night. Or, if you fantasise about being taken 'against your will' to be used in a harem, he could be called the Sultan of Sex. Ask him to name you – you might be surprised by the naughty nicknames he comes up with. This little tip is at least guaranteed to give you a good laugh whether or not it turns you on. A final little tip is that you can then send him a red hot, X-rated text and include his new naughty nickname in your message.

Dare to Go There

Sometimes, from a man's perspective, the best fantasy play involves daring to go places (not literally 'going places', but chatting about them) you wouldn't normally go to with your sex chat. Men can be such naughty creatures and given some permission will tell you all sorts of dirty things. Light some candles, lie back together and ask him to tell you one fantasy that he's kept secret – and tell him you'll then share one with him. For example, ask him if he's ever fantasised about a threesome with you and your best friend. A final tip: remember to never ask about a fantasy topic if there is a potential answer you don't want to hear!

Sextion Five

All Sorts of Sexy Tips
for His Pleasure

There are so many ways you can turn him on that take little or no energy on your part. Putting some of these into action will make all the difference to his – and your – sexual enjoyment.

Suck Those Fingers

Let me remind you again that men are incredibly visual creatures. When you use your body language to give them signs and signals of sexual interest they pay attention! So let your fingers do the talking in this little tip. Select something tasty that he likes, for example, it could be something like chocolate sauce, strawberry jam or honey. Pre-plan this and have the pot at the bedside. Then, without saying anything, but obviously in front of him, sensually dip a couple of your fingers in the pot and scoop out a little of the sauce. Next, slowly lick the sauce from your fingertips in an erotic fashion before leaning over and giving him a big sexy kiss with the stickiness on your lips. Really go to town with this and lick every last drop off your fingertips.

Then, slip a finger back in the pot and gently dab some of the sauce on to his lips. You can then gently lick and kiss it off. Now you can really get sexy with that pot of sauce – lean back, scoop some more out with your fingertips and run it across your pubic bone and down your labia. He'll be gagging to lick that sauce off!

The Scoop Technique

Think of using the whole flat of your hand, with your fingertips together, forming a scoop. You can use a whole flash of your hand during sex-play to scoop right from the base of his bottom, up his perineum to his testicles, and over his penis. Done like a gentle massage technique it gives a fantastic sensation. Imagine you two are already naked and you're touching and caressing in your foreplay. Slosh some lubricant into the palm of your hand, nudge his thighs apart, and do this upwards scooping motion. Repeat it a few times.

You can also do this in a position like the Classic Missionary. Imagine that he's thrusting slowly and sensually – reach for the lubricant (it should always be on your bedside table!), put some on your hand and reach around to scoop right up from where his thighs meet his lower buttocks, right over his crack, and to his lower back. It's both a sensual and a relaxing movement.

Tempting Teasing

Always look for little tricks that will tease him – particularly visual teases. There's no way a man can resist a bit of Tempting Teasing. Let's say you two are mucking around, sit astride him (even if you still have your clothes on) and slowly unbutton your top. Then cup your breasts in your hands, jiggle them around, lean forward to brush them across his face and then sit back upright. The trick is not to let him touch! He can only watch as you stroke your nipples until they spring to life, and swirl your fingertips around them. Again, lean forward to nuzzle them across his face – tempting and teasing him with the sight of you stroking your breasts.

Whip Him into Shape

Having just talked about fantasies, and in particular some where the woman takes the dominant role, use this trick to get him in the mood for some role play or gentle bondage and domination. Obviously you need to have trust if you're going to get into tying each other up. Let's say you've been enjoying a bit of foreplay, ask him if he'd like to be tied up to a chair. Tell him he can trust you! Once tied to a chair take something like the cord from yours or his dressing gown and strut around him threatening to whip him. What you do though is actually whip the floor at his feet. Keep up the pretence of threatening to whip him but keep striking the floor instead. This will get his blood pumping!

Get 'Em Off

Here's the simplest little tip that women don't tend to think of. A man may want his partner to strip off for him – or she may want him to strip off for her. But being undressed by your lover is a really sexy experience. Turn the tables on him, as usually it's the woman who gets undressed by her partner. Take charge and undress him: undo the zip on his trousers while you remark about 'unleashing his breast'. Remember to have fun with those naughty nicknames! Push him back on to the bed and slowly peel off his trousers. Then unbutton his shirt while you compliment him on his physique. He'll love the fact that you're being dominating while getting him stripped off.

Masturbate Him

Every man loves the occasional hand job. Often it reminds them of their first sexual experiences when their girlfriend wasn't ready to go all the way but offered a hand job instead. Many women think 'why bother?', but you can score loads of points with him by masturbating him. That's because, to a man, having a hand job is easy and a bit sexy and dirty. You can whisper in his ear that you want to pleasure him with your hand only. A big tip is to talk dirty to him while you do it. Change hands if your hand gets tired and always keep asking him if you're using the right speed and pressure.

And, do you know what's great about giving him a hand job? Well, fair's fair when it comes to the etiquette of sex, so you can ask him to return the pleasure and get you off with his hand or his hand plus a vibrator.

Staying Power

I've already mentioned my most important tip to enhance a man's staying power, which is for him to work out his pelvic floor muscles. Lasting longer is one of the most common concerns a man has. It causes them a great deal of anxiety and many of the mail bags I've had in various places I've worked have contained letters from men wanting to have more staying power.

Here are a couple more top tips to help him gain control. First of all, choose a position where you know he gets less stimulation. Think about it – in positions where he's getting a lot of friction, and all over his penis, he's going to get more excited. Of course, it varies between men and depends on their size and shape, and also the size of the woman they are sleeping with, which positions give them too much stimulation. But, that said, any position where she's opened up wide as in Doggy style, Spoons with her upper leg lifted upwards, Unfold the Flower or Girls on Top, provide slightly less direct stimulation all over his penis.

The next tip is one that few people even think of and that's to suggest he masturbates earlier in the day if you two are planning a sexy evening. Often men need their partner's 'permission' to do this, but it will definitely help him to last longer the second time around with you. There's another great tip that works well if a couple uses condoms. If this is the case, he can put on two condoms and this cuts down on his sensations. Finally, a great tip is to change positions fairly frequently. If you start in the Classic Missionary position, you can change to you on top or him behind. When his stimulation is interrupted, it helps him to last longer. Obviously a change of position interrupts your stimulation too, so it's important for you to keep a vibrator handy to keep stimulating yourself or use your hands to keep stimulating yourself while positions are changed.

The Classic Tit Fuck

Sometimes we do things for a man simply because we know they love them. It may not turn us on but hopefully it doesn't turn us off! This applies to putting what he sees as your beautiful breasts to good work – and letting him thrust between them. This is usually most comfortable if you sit on the edge of the bed and he stands between your feet, because that way his penis is at about the height of your breasts. Or, you can lie sideways on the bed and across the width of the bed. He can then lie next to you but shimmy further up, so that again his penis is at your breast level. You could also sit on a kitchen chair (for some spontaneous sex) and again he stands in front of you.

A big tip is to grip his buttocks from behind to help him keep between your breasts. This works better when you leave your bra on, but then you slip your straps down so your breasts are exposed. Or you can squeeze your breasts together for him.

You may not want a 'pearl necklace' so definitely let him know you want him to come on your stomach or into his hand or a tissue.

Sexy Smells

This is the perfect tip for when either of you has to go away and you don't want him to forget you – not that he would! Wear a pair of your knickers around for a couple of hours. This way they absorb your very own unique scent. Now slip them under his pillow and leave him a note telling him your 'heaven scent' awaits him. Your sexy knickers will be lightly covered with your smell and he can masturbate to it. After all, why do you think there's a roaring trade on the Internet for worn knickers? Because men are sexually aroused by a woman's smell.

Foot Fancy

If you think the man in your life has a hankering after feet then why not try this sexy little trick. Buy a new pair of very high-heeled shoes and greet him while wearing them. Don't take them off during foreplay and when the time comes to slip into bed, tell him you are going to keep them on. Make sure they're real 'fuck me' shoes! In bed, you can do plenty of things that involve your feet, like allowing him to kiss his way down your stockinged thigh and admiring how sexy your feet look in your high heels. Go for a position like Unfold the Flower as before.

Foot Fuck

This is an interesting little technique that some couples find really erotic or at least great fun. Imagine you kneel on the edge of the bed or the sofa with him behind you. This way your feet hang over the edge and then you close them together. He then kneels on the floor facing your feet and he can pull them down slightly so that his penis can fit between your soles which you are holding together. He then thrusts in and out of your soles. For a man with a bit of a foot fetish this is absolute heaven. And for a couple that are a bit sexperimental, it's certainly something a bit novel.

There you are, with plenty of tips to use on the man in your life – or as a man to suggest that your lover tries on you – it's now time to think about some sexy tips, tricks and techniques for couples to try in Part Three.

Part Three

Tips, Tricks and Techniques for Both of You

Sexction One

Tips to Use with Rude Foods

We have to eat for nourishment but there's a huge amount of pleasure to be gained from a little rude-food play. You can turn everyday foods into something very sensual and pleasurable with these tips, tricks and techniques. Rude-food play will often set the scene for an evening of pleasurable sex.

Honey Heaven

Honey is so sticky and lovely that it's fantastic to use in sex-play. Not only that, it's good for you too! You can keep a pot by your bedside to dip into during foreplay. Here's a little trick: lick your finger before you dip it into the pot and the honey will come off your finger more easily as you roll it around your lover's nipples or lips. Without licking and dipping first, the honey will stick as much to your finger as it does to their erogenous zones.

You can even turn some simple tea and toast into something flirtatious. Why not surprise your lover by making them tea and toast in bed that includes some luscious golden honey to smear on the toast and each other! Watch it dribble off the spoon onto his penis or her labia.

Melon Delight

Juicy, tropical melon simply looks suggestive and erotic! It can be turned into a seductive dessert or simply brought to bed on a platter to play with. What you can do is take some pieces of ripe, sweet melon chunks and trace them around her nipples. As little droplets of juice tumble down her breasts you can lap up every little drop. Use this tip to continue stimulating her breasts with your tongue and lips. She can also give you some yummy pleasure by dripping some melon juice down your chest and gently licking the droplets.

Fabulous Foot Play

Make sure your lover's feet are fresh and clean; nicely scrubbed up in a shower or bath before you begin. Then take a bunch of freshly washed grapes and ask her to lie back on the bed. Use your fingertips to gently slip a grape between each of her toes and then carefully nibble the grapes one at a time. Not only will she feel like a Sex Goddess when you treat her this way but you'll feel like the King of Sex with this sophisticated trick. Fewer women than men are interested in their lover's feet – it seems to be a male-dominated fetish – but if you love his feet by all means treat him to this little pleasure.

Luscious Lover's Pass Kiss

This is a wonderful kiss for sharing something creamy like a piece of chocolate. Open up a bar and place one square between your lips. Tell your lover you're going to share it with them. Suck it until it's warmed up and then move in for a kiss. Take your time and then carefully pass the piece of warmed-up chocolate from your mouth to your lover's. This is a delicious and sensual kiss but the tip is to do it when you've already enjoyed a little foreplay and you're both turned on. If you haven't been kissing and caressing for at least a little time before you do this trick, it can seem a bit over the top.

Nyataimori Nights Inspiration

This Japanese speciality of allowing paid customers to feast off reclining glamorous women, who have food beautifully placed around their bodies, can be re-created in your own home. Select some favourite foods that can be placed around your body and become your lover's feast or dessert! Tasty little cakes and nibbles are by far the best things to use. You can do this in your sitting room or bedroom by spreading out comfortable and soft blankets, and light the area with candles. Make sure the room is warm and if your lover isn't supremely confident, they can keep their knickers on as you create a light feast across their body. You want this experience to be fun and pleasurable and not stressful.

Hand Feeding Heaven

There's a real art to hand feeding your lover. It takes sensitivity and skill to do it in a sensual way. Here are some tips to help you do it successfully: to begin with, anything like hand feeding is best done by candlelight because it adds to the atmosphere. Next, make sure things are in bite-sized or small pieces. Always take your time when hand feeding. Don't shove anything into your lover's mouth but always gently place it between their lips. As you touch their mouth to put something into it, you can then run your fingers around their lips.

Belly-Button Bliss

The belly button is a much-neglected erogenous zone. But because of its location, it is very sensitive to careful touch. Here's a perfect little tip to enjoy when you're sharing your favourite liqueur. As you sip from your liqueur glass, stroke your partner's stomach and then move to their belly button. Circle it lightly with your index finger. Ask them to lie back and then pour a tiny bit of the liqueur into it. Now, gently lap it out of their belly button and you'd be amazed at their physical response. Because this erogenous zone is located just above their pubic area it heightens their sensitivity there as you stimulate the belly button.

As you lap against the edges of their belly button you can also begin to rub your fingers back and forth over their pubic area to heighten their pleasure. Just make sure their belly button is clean before you do this!

Delicious Dessert

This tip is a scaled-down version of Nyataimori Nights Inspiration. This only requires a piece or two of delicious chocolate – as well as his desire to do some tongue-action! During foreplay, break off a square or two of chocolate. Slip them on to her pubic mound and continue foreplay where your fingertips make sweeping circles on this area. Now, go down between her legs and with your fingertips move the melting chocolate to between her labia. Gently push it inwards with your tongue and continue lapping. As it melts you'll enjoy the taste of the chocolate melting and mixing with her juices and she'll love the creamy sensation. There is a legend that Mick Jagger did this with a whole Mars Bar – not quite so subtle!

Spice is Nice

There is definitely some truth to the belief that some foods act as aphrodisiacs. One potent truth is the fact that certain spices can help with sexual arousal. They do so by getting your juices flowing by helping to dilate (open up) the blood vessels. Any spicy dish containing chilli, onions or garlic will help with dilation. The flush you see on someone's face when they've eaten a hot and spicy dish is due to their facial vessels dilating. If you imagine that the vessels can dilate all over the body – including the genitals – you can understand why a spicy meal can help lead to you having spicy sex. After all, engorgement of the genitals is a key sign of sexual arousal and you need to have a good flow of blood to get engorgement. The top tip is not to make the food so spicy that it upsets your stomach. Also, keep portions small and both eat the same spicy foods so you have the same flavours in your mouth.

The Seductive Secret of Dark Chocolate

Dark chocolate is another aphrodisiac food with a proven track record. The darker the chocolate, the better, as quality dark chocolate contains high levels of healthy antioxidants and PEA – phenylethyamine – a feel-good chemical. So, it's not a myth that chocolate is seductive and has aphrodisiac powers – not only does it look sensual but the taste is fabulous and the creaminess of it on the tongue is erotic.

Anyway, introducing fine quality chocolate to your dining or the bedside is a positive thing to do! From sipping hot chocolate together, to sliding a piece of melting chocolate between your mouths, or spoon-feeding each other any chocolate-based dessert – you can enhance your sex-play.

Erotic Eclair

Men love mixing up a bit of food play with sex-play. This trick will definitely turn him on! When you know you're in the mood for sex-play, buy some gorgeous, cream-filled, chocolate eclairs. Arrange them on a plate that's going to be handy when foreplay begins. Take control at some point and ask him to lie back and enjoy what you're going to do. Kiss and lick his penis until it becomes erect and then open up one of the eclairs and encase his shaft in it. An important tip is that as long as it's at room temperature and not straight out of the fridge he won't lose his erection. Now you can tease and tickle his shaft while you nibble and lick at the eclair with his erection encased inside it.

If you can't get any eclairs then a jam doughnut carefully cut in half can be used in the same way.

Sensual Salad Dressing

Some other important ingredients for rude-food play include natural aphrodisiacs like ginger and ginseng. Both of these increase circulation and get that all-important blood pumping and help with vessel dilation. The easiest tip for introducing ginger and ginseng into food play is through a salad dressing. Mix up your usual salad dressing and toss in a generous pinches of ginger and/or ginseng. You can get ginseng capsules (and sometimes a powder form) from health-food shops. Simply break open a capsule and mix into the dressing. Ginger, of course, is available from any supermarket. Not only does this make a tasty dressing but hopefully will help put you in the mood.

Seductive Strawberries

One of the most seductive treats you can share, and that's fantastic
for hand feeding each other, are strawberries dipped in warm
chocolate. Not only do they look beautiful but they taste scrump-
tious. Warm up some top quality chocolate (or use a fondue set for
this) and dip strawberries into the warm chocolate, swirl them
around, and place them in your lover's mouth. Another little trick is
to make your strawberries into sex toys. Once you've dipped them
into the chocolate ask your lover to lie back and you can swirl the
chocolate around her nipples. Check that the chocolate is only
warm and not hot! Then you can lick the warm chocolate off her
nipples before biting into the strawberry.

Wanton Whipped Cream

Whipped cream is not only naughty – because we all know it's
chock-full of calories – but also because it's creamy and sensuous.
What is especially fantastic about whipped cream is that you can
buy it in a spray-can to put to good use! So keep some handy for
your sex-play. Then once her top is off, ask if you can carefully spray
some whipped cream around her breasts. The coolness of it will
make her skin tingle and you can use your fingertips to swirl it
around her breasts and down her abdomen, as well as using your
tongue to lap at it.

The next stop is to spray her pubic mound and labia with it – a
great way to kick-off oral pleasure!

Rude-Food Fun

I've already mentioned the fact that people can get too hung up on sex, and it all becomes too serious. If this is the case for you two, you should definitely have some frolics and fun with rude food. Why not serve up little 'nipple cakes' for dessert? These are little iced fairy cakes topped with a tiny glacé cherry in the centre. Or, why not take bananas, cut in half, filled with cream, and topped at the end with a little cherry for your very own penis-lookalike desserts! Be creative and put suggestive-looking cakes on a platter for an evening of fun. Many specialist bakers now supply sexy-looking desserts.

Home, Sexy Home

People forget the importance of the sense of smell in seducing their lover. If you know your lover has a favourite scent or thing to eat then be creative in seducing them by their sense of smell. For example, if you know they adore the smell of cinnamon then place a cinnamon stick on a baking tray in a low oven before they come over. By the time they get there, your whole house will be infused with the scent of cinnamon. Or, if they love chocolate, you can microwave a mug of hot chocolate and place it to the side of your sofa. The scent of chocolate will waft around as you kiss and caress them. This is one reason why scented candles are so popular because when you stimulate one sense, the others spring to life, too.

Sexy Splodging

Some people have a fetish called 'splodging' where they love to smear, play with, and roll around in, cream cakes and buns and any erotic food. In fact splodgers have organised events where groups of people will roll about in all sorts of mixtures and rude foods. For most people the mess is too much to make this a viable option to have a little fun with. However you can get into some mini-splodging and protect your bedding – either by putting some old (but clean) sheets on top of your regular ones or spreading out some soft, old, clean towels across your bed. Then let go for some good, 'dirty' fun – have some cream cakes to hand to splodge on each other and roll around in – you might end up enjoying this bit of fetish play or at least learn to let some of your inhibitions slip away.

Sextion Two

Playful Tips

Many people I come across have forgotten that sex is about
enjoyment! They've lost the all-important ability to let go a little
and then, unfortunately, they get too serious about sex. There's
nothing wrong with having fun and laughing with each other in bed
but there's everything wrong with laughing at your partner over
something. Just be aware of the difference.

Blind Man in the Buff – What Are You
Being Touched With?

This is a naughty sex game that guarantees to give you lots of
pleasure. It also helps develop sexual trust between a couple –
something that even long-standing couples might lack. All you need
is a blindfold and your imagination! If you don't have a proper
blindfold from an erotic shop (and why not keep one in your
bedside pleasure chest? (see later)) then anything soft and silky like
a scarf will do.

You can take turns doing this so both of you get the chance to
be pleasured in this playful way. One of you is stripped off
(although if you're building trust you might want to leave sexy

knickers on) and blindfolded. Make sure they're lying comfortably in bed or on a sofa. Now the other one touches and teases the blindfolded partner with their fingertips, their tongue, their lips, and sex toys. The blindfolded partner has to guess what they're being touched with – harder than you'd imagine! For example, the tip of your tongue might feel like the tip of your fingers with lubricant on them.

69 Is Fine

Never underestimate the pleasure of 69! The two main variations are lying facing each other, both on your sides, top to toe. This gives her access to his penis and him access to her vagina. Or one of you lies flat on their back and the other straddles them, again top to toe. But don't just lap at each other's genitals! Try teasing the other with your fingertips, making little tiny strokes around and around or little tiny 'petting' actions. You can swap between touching and tasting each other with tongues and lips. Also a fantastic trick during 69 – for you both – is to use sex toys on each other at the same time. This is managed best in the version of 69 when you're both lying on your sides. It gives you a fantastic view of exactly what you are stimulating with the tip of the vibrator!

Advanced PC Muscle Action

I've already mentioned squeezing and releasing your PC muscles during penetration. But once you've gained PC muscle strength a fantastic sensation can be created by the long-squeeze technique. Rather than the pulsating action I've described previously, the advanced trick is to squeeze and hold during three or four penetrative thrusts. He'll feel like he's been gripped in a vice – and the friction created against his thrusting can be powerful and pleasurable for both partners.

Lust on a Lilo

A fun and feisty little tip for summer sex! Have a lilo blown up and to hand in your bathroom. Now run a warm and sudsy bath. Add some gorgeous ylang-ylang aromatherapy bath oil that has a sensual scent. After enjoying some sex-play in the bath, climb out and enjoy a gentle romp on the lilo. If your bathroom's too small, then spread out a blanket on the bedroom floor and place the lilo on it. The lilo will give you a new and different sensation when you have sex on it.

Strap On Sex

Contrary to popular belief, the majority of strap-on dildos are sold to straight couples rather than lesbian couples. Many men (and their partners) love experimenting with strap-on sex. A great way to raise the idea of it, is to introduce it during fantasy chat. Doesn't fantasy chat have a lot to answer for! He may well have been thinking about it and simply needs 'permission' to express his desire to find out more. Many couples find that incorporating strap-on sex into a dominant-submissive scenario frees the man up even more. He loses his inhibitions because he's 'submitting to her desire' for sexual dominance. As with any anal sex play always use loads of lubricant and start gently!

Double-ended Pleasure

Sticking with some anal play for him, a dildo to maximise both partner's pleasure at the same time can come from double-ended dildos. The length on such a dildo is long enough for her to insert one end into her vagina and for him to insert one end into his anus. What you can do is shimmy your genitals up towards each other so that you can both be penetrated at the same time. For him to be anally penetrated, he can lie back and twist on his side so that his bottom is near to her pelvis. The fun begins once you insert the ends into yourselves. You need to begin slowly and carefully to establish a rocking motion. Once you've got the hang of it many couples enjoy this type of sex-perimentation.

Your Water Magic

For some reason we humans are drawn to water play. There are some fantastic waterproof vibrators you can come by for some bath-time bliss together. I highly recommend the G-spot Aqua Vibe with its 'come over here' crooked-finger design. When you two have been lathering each other up and enjoying a little bit of foreplay in the water you can then use this to stimulate her vagina. Let her lie back and relax while you stimulate her.

Come and Get It

This is a great little sex game for two reasons – it's easy to do and you can be as creative as you want to. One of you is 'it' and gets to be inventive. The other of you waits, perhaps enjoying a glass of wine, while the other prepares the 'game' for sex. They get to go off and choose the room and location (it could be the bathroom, the bedroom, the kitchen counter, a floor or a sofa), as well as the type of things to go along with the lovemaking. For example, if they choose the bathroom then they may choose something like the G-spot Aqua Vibe to place in the bath. They can light candles or use dim lighting and have sexy rude food to hand – or whatever

they want. When their scene is set, they can ring you on your
mobile or simply call out, 'Come and get it!' The next time you play
this game, you swap roles.

Rub a Dub Dub

A simple and easy pleasure technique for both of you! Many
women don't masturbate with their hands or sex toys – they
masturbate by rubbing themselves against a pillow or the palm of
their hand. Give each other permission to rub your genitals against
each other to get off. Tell your partner you want them to rub
themselves silly against you! This is definitely a great trick to use
with a woman who has an overly sensitive clitoris – she can show
her partner just how gently she likes to rub herself by rubbing
against his thigh.

Penis Play

There are some fantastic vibrators designed to slip over the shaft of
a man's penis that will give both of you loads of pleasure. Most sit
at the base of his penis and offer various attachments that would
tickle her clitoris and vibrate his shaft. The best thing about these
is that they can add to your sensations without any effort on your
part! He slips it on, turns it on, and you both get a nice little
vibration.

Feminising Fun

Gender-bending has been around for ages and has become
increasingly popular with people who like to sex-periment. It takes
a fairly confident man to admit to wanting to try a little

feminisation. This is nothing to do with being gay or straight and has everything to do with playing around with things like becoming a little more submissive and stepping out of the traditional masculine role. Frequently, a couple only figures out that he'd like to try a little feminisation – or that she'd like to feminise him – when they've been having a little bit of fantasy chat that strays into this territory. So, this is a great way to sound out how your partner feels about this.

Remember, feminising can be simply about putting a little bit of mascara on him or going the whole hog and letting him slip into stockings, silk panties and lots of make-up. This is completely up to the couple but you may want to start with something plainer, a bit more 'vanilla', like putting some lipgloss and mascara on him for starters. Once he's been feminised – even only a little of the way – you'd be surprised how easy it is to swap your roles around when it comes to sex.

Going Commando

Having a little bit of secret sex-play between you two can really liven up your sex life. One little trick is for both of you to agree to go commando (no underpants/knickers) when you're going out to dinner or to a friend's party. This means there's easy access to each other's genitals, particularly for him to reach under her skirt when, say, innocently looking at a restaurant menu. Or perhaps, when both of you excuse yourselves to go in to the kitchen to help out at a friend's party and have a quick grope of each other's privates!

Another little tip is to surprise your partner by going commando and then only telling them once you're out and about somewhere. Imagine standing in the slightly deserted aisle of a supermarket or behind a clothes rack at a clothes store when you can whisper that 'if you have a little grope you will get a surprise!' The sexiest fun can be had from the smallest of tricks, like this one.

Ring a Ding Ding – Cock Ring Stimulation

A little trick for helping him last longer is for him to try out a cock ring. There are different styles but the basic principle is that it sits at the base of his erect penis – and as it's engorged with blood, as long as the cock ring is in place, the blood doesn't flow back out. Many men report that they get extra firmness with their erection and that it is longer-lasting. Of the different types of rings available, I highly recommend using flexible cock rings as these have a little 'give' for ease of placement.

A great tip is for the woman to learn how to slip it over his penis and testicles – so follow the instructions! But accompany this little process with some sexy chat about how gorgeous his manhood looks and how you can't wait to feel his big hard-on inside you. The woman can also be responsible for lightly lubricating it for more comfort but the man should do any final adjustments so that he's comfortable. While you're getting so much enjoyment from his erection don't forget a cock ring should never be used for more than 20 minutes. Once you get the hang of using one there are various attachments that can be added to cock rings. There are little stimulators, or ticklers, for her or mini-weights to give him a sensation that his scrotum is being slightly pulled away from his body – remember the previous tip I gave you in Picking the Plums in Part 2?

Your Personal Pleasure Chest

I briefly mentioned earlier about you having a 'pleasure chest' at your bedside. This is what a wise couple (or a wise single!) puts together and keeps handy for spontaneous sex. Put all your favourite things that enhance your sex life in your pleasure chest – use a lockable one if you have children about. What should you include? Everything, from a great supply of condoms, to your sex toys. Keep your favourite lubricants in it as well as a pot of honey or your favourite flavour of jam. You might also want to put in it things like a blindfold, handcuffs, a cock ring, silky stockings, your favourite erotica or sexy magazines, edible body paint, and other little items like a feather for feathering and a body brush.

A-zone Arousal

Most people know about the G-spot and for women who are sensitive there, having this coin-sized area stimulated can be a sensational experience. But let's not forget about the whole A-zone! In recent years, sex researchers have spoken of the neglected anterior fornix. Imagine this area as located at the front (tummy side) vaginal wall from the G-spot (a couple inches up) upwards to her cervix. This area is packed with nerve endings in the delicate tissue that can be stimulated with different sex positions and sex toys. Try circular style thrusting, where a man uses his hips to form little circles, which rubs this whole area with the end of his penis.

Double Hander Delight

Forget 'two heads' – two hands are definitely better than one, so put them both to good use! For her – if she's lying on her back you can crouch above her and use one hand to massage each of her breasts in matching circular motions. Even better, use the fingertips of one hand to lightly brush back and forth across her two nipples while your other hand gently massages her pubic mound, just glancing along her clitoral region and upper labia. And for him – she can always use a double-hander technique when stimulating his penis with one hand. Kneel to the side of his hips and with your other hand rub gently between his thighs back and forth over his perineum.

Raunchy Remote Control

Again, I've got sexy secrets for you two to share. There are some fantastic remote-controlled vibrators to have fun with. You can, obviously, place the remote-controlled vibrator (depending on the design) inside her vagina or on her clitoris, or wherever you want, and while you're kissing and caressing, you can occasionally hit the button to turn it on. But one sexy tip is to take this sex-play out of doors. She can have the vibrator in place when you're, say, at a bar or at a friend's and no one will know when you hit the button to start it, except her. Just think of the smile on her face as you two try and hold a conversation with your friends, or when you're out shopping, and you've turned on the remote control.

Mystery Sex

Sometimes, asking to try a new technique can feel a bit daunting, even for long-standing couples. For any number of reasons, people can get a little shy. This little tip helps you get over that. Because we all have secret desires, it will help you two get to try them out. All you need is a notepad and then both of you write down two or three sexual techniques you've wanted to experiment with – each on a separate piece of the notepaper. All the pieces of paper are folded in half, mark them with your initials, and mix them up.

In advance, give each other permission to be honest about the things you want to try. You now each select one folded piece of paper and read it aloud. A little tip is to try to read it in a low, sensual voice rather then a nervous one! Try doing this by candlelight or with the dimmer switch down to help create a sensual mood. Having given each other permission to be honest on your pieces of notepaper you now have to try out the suggestions.

Control Yourself

This sex game is a great technique for learning how to control yourselves – particularly if one of you is too quick when it comes to your lovemaking. Again, you need a notepad and both of you should write down something that you want 'controlled'. You also write down your codeword that goes with this. For example, if she wants him to do five thrusts only on the command of her codeword, then withdraw, and then stimulate her with his hands or mouth – she writes this down along with her codeword. That means that during penetrative sex, when she says the codeword, after five thrusts he has to withdraw and continue with what was agreed on the paper. This technique builds up anticipation and sexual arousal. It's meant to be fun so if, say, the man has a problem with premature ejaculation, this isn't the technique to use with him while he's trying to learn to have better control over his ejaculation.

X Marks the Spot

This is a sizzling and fun little technique where you can discover a bit more about each other's favourite erogenous zones. It's a great one to do when you've had a couple drinks and you feel like being uninhibited with each other. You do need two big pieces of plain or graph paper – one for each of you. They need to be the length of your bodies, so you may have to Sellotape pieces together. Lie down on the paper and with a pen or pencil your lover traces around your body with the pen. Then you swap places and the other lies on the second sheet of paper and has their body traced. Now, be playful and mark with the pen on the paper, within your body 'outlines', Xs on each of your favourite erogenous zones.

This can just be a learning exercise because you both get to see where the other marks their favourite spots with Xs. But it can turn into a fully fledged sex game where you take turns exploring each and every one of those Xs and the corresponding points on your lover's body. You can make a rule that each X has to be explored with a vibrator, or your tongue or your fingertips – whatever rule you feel like making!

Sex Slave Massage

This is a great tip for when you're in the mood for a little bit of submissive-dominant sex chat or role play. One of you is completely spoilt by the Sex Slave – but take turns and the next time the other gets to be spoilt. Light some candles and have a lovely soft towel, massage oils and playthings to hand. Warm the towels on the radiator or take them from the airing cupboard and wrap the master/mistress in them. As you massage one part of their body, for example their arm, keep the rest of them wrapped up in the warm towels for their comfort.

Using delicate and sensual movements, rub some gorgeous massage oil into their body. Once you've sensitised most of their body to your touch, bring out the playthings – a feather to do some feathering along their erogenous zones. Or their favourite vibrator, to gently tease them with. And finally, ask them what their 'pleasure is' – how you can finish them off – through oral sex, manual stimulation or penetrative sex.

A Little Porn Pleasure

There's absolutely nothing wrong with consenting adults enjoying a little bit of pornography. Obviously, I'm talking about legal porn. It's how you approach the topic that counts. Here are my top tips – always ask first if your partner's interested in watching some porn – don't just put on a porn DVD to play. Start with something gentle – some 'vanilla' porn that won't seem threatening to them. Don't exclaim about how sexy the porn stars are as it will undermine how your partner feels about their body. Don't start shagging in the middle of it unless your partner also wants to, as they may find it very offensive that you want to watch porn while you shag them! If you both enjoy porn, keep it for special occasions – people can become reliant on it and then find they can't get aroused without it. That's not a healthy sex life!

Naughty Nipple Clamps

Just a little bit of experimentation with the pain-pleasure borderline can liven up your sex life. One of the easiest tips for doing this is to experiment with nipple clamps. You can buy these at most adult shops or online. They should only be as painful as you want them to be! Slip them on during foreplay or agree to wear them during penetrative sex. You can buy his and hers sets so that he can experience a bit of pain with his pleasure, too. Some couples end up experimenting with clamps on her labia and his scrotum – again this is an individual preference, but if you want to try a little bit of pain it's one way of doing so. As with all these things, don't leave them on too long – 5 or 10 minutes is plenty! And if you have sensitive skin or bruise easily you ought to be aware that such sex-play may not be for you.

Blindfolded Lust

You can increase your sensory sensitivity when you take away one sense, which makes you appreciate the others more. An ideal way of doing this is to put blindfolds on each other at some point during foreplay. Once you're blindfolded, you'll be amazed at how quickly your skin comes to life as you are touched, and as you touch your lover. And when you kiss, you'll be able to taste your lover's mouth and skin more clearly.

Not only is this an incredibly sensual technique to try, but you can also have fun with it as you generally feel your way round each other's bodies. When you start penetrative sex, it can really heighten sexual enjoyment. You won't want to take the blindfolds off!

Mobile Magic

There's talking dirty and there's talking dirty in a sexy way! Phone sex can give you loads of pleasure. You might find that what you think would be embarrassing actually frees you up and you become less inhibited speaking on the phone than when talking in bed together. But to avoid feeling embarrassed, how about trying some Mobile Magic. These are a few crucial tips to use during phone sex. Always use words you feel comfortable with when talking dirty. Start slowly and remember to use a lower and sensual vocal tone rather than one that's high-pitched and stressed! Describe in vivid detail exactly what you are doing to yourself – how you're touching your breasts or clitoris, or stroking your penis. Describe how you're getting aroused and the signs of it – like how engorged your penis is getting, or erect your nipples are. Let your imagination go as you build your confidence and to tell your lover what you would do to them if they were there with you at that moment.

Sextion Three

Downright Dirty and
Very Rude Tips

Here are some seriously sexy tips, tricks and techniques – some of
which are not for the faint hearted. Read this section together and
perhaps you may be able to build up the courage to try some of the
racier ones or at least make them part of your fantasy chat. For
example, you may decide as a man that you don't really want to
experience a Pro Job (Tip No.1) but you might turn discussing it
into some fantasy chat. Let these tips – or at least the idea of these
tips – push your sex life a little bit further.

Mindblowing Pro Jobs

I was told about Pro Jobs (I've now coined this term because I think
it aptly describes the technique) when meeting sex workers in a TV
Green Room. I had the chance to ask them about some of the
things that men requested that they might not ask their wives and
partners. I really wasn't surprised when this was graphically
described to me. Basically, what a Pro Job is, is a blow job with your
finger stuck up your man's bottom!

Of course you need to do this technique with finesse. Use lots of lubrication and to prevent direct contact between your finger and their anus, either slip your finger into a condom or use a latex glove or some such thing. Begin by gently giving them a blow job and tickling around their anal opening with a well-lubricated fingertip. When he feels relaxed, you gradually slip it in. This gives you a chance to stimulate his prostate gently – located a couple of inches up on what I'll describe as the 'inside' wall of his anus. The inside wall being the one 'underneath' his perineum (the area between his testicles and anus). Men can have mind-blowing blow jobs with this technique. A great tip is the fact that this can speed things up for him if she's getting 'blowers cramp' – tired cheek muscles from opening her mouth to give him a blow job.

Butt Plug Love

Both men and women can wear butt plugs – they're not just for gay men! They come in different sizes to accommodate, well, different sizes of bottom. There are a couple of different tricks you can try. Many couples buy a matching pair of butt plugs (often a bigger one for him) and wear them around when they do, say, the weekly shop on a Saturday morning. Both of them know that the other is also getting aroused by this stimulation and it's their sexy little secret.

But another great trick for you two to try is to leave the butt plugs in when you're having penetrative sex. This will definitely heighten your pleasure and seems a bit naughty at the same time. Both men and women report that it gives them intense pleasure.

Faux Water Sports

Water sports are more popular than you'd think which is why I'm mentioning them here. However, the danger of transmission of infection is high and so I completely recommend that people experiment with 'faux' water sports. Just in case you're not in the know, water sports involve urinating on your partner or in more extreme cases a man urinates into a hose that's inserted into his partner's vagina. This is very risky! It sounds disgusting to some, but for those of you who are interested in such things why not try faking it?

The best way I can think of is to brew some weak tea – chamomile looks the most realistic. Get your partner to lie face down as you drip it on to their back (definitely test on your inner wrist first to make sure it's not too hot!) and do all the dirty talk that might accompany water sports. Or your partner can get in the bath and you stand over them, but again, you just pour the innocent tea over them rather than urinating on them. This is where fantasy play can work a treat – if you get into it as a fantasy and role play, and really go for it in terms of dirty talk, you can re-create water sports safely.

Bottoms Up

Many men love to have their bottoms tickled and teased during foreplay or sex but often feel a little inhibited about admitting it. You can reserve a vibrator just for his pleasure and as suggested in Part Two under Oral Sex Tips for Him, you can begin by teasing his perineum with it as you give him some oral pleasure. When you've got him captive with lust, you can ask him if you can gently use it on his bottom. As with any anal-play, you need loads of lubricant and you need to start slowly. Tickle and tease the rim of his anus with little circular motions with the tip of the vibrator. As his sphincter relaxes you can start to ease the tip of it in. Once you're skilled at this, this is a great trick to do to him when you're in the Classic Missionary position. Have the lubricant and vibrator ready during foreplay. Once he's inside you in the Missionary position, you can gently start the 'rimming' with the tip of the vibrator before partially inserting it during gentle thrusting. You can either hold it steady as he continues to thrust, so he gets the vibrating sensations, or, at his request, you can move it in and out a little bit – it just depends on his preference.

A View for Two

As long as you're both in agreement, and it's not done under any pressure, one great trick for spicing things up is for a couple to enjoy an occasional visit to a high quality lap-dancing club together. Not only do they find the visual experience arousing – and it gets them hot for having sex back at home – but it can also provide a great deal of material for fantasy play further down the line. This is true for any visual stimulus that a couple has seen together (including seeing an erotic scene in a film, reading sexy magazines or watching porn) – they can talk about it at other times and remember how much they enjoyed it. Recalling in detail something sexy they've seen together is a great way to open up a more honest communication with each other in bed.

Display and Play

She needs to be comfortable with this and then you can both have loads of fun with her tied up. Carefully tie her ankles with a soft dressing-gown cord – or any other suitable soft fabric. But you need to tie her ankles separately so that her legs are completely opened up. She can be lying on the bed and you tie one ankle to one leg of the bed and the other ankle to the other side. Or, she can be sitting in a chair and you tie her ankles so that one's tied to one chair leg and the other is tied to the opposite chair leg. Again her legs are wide open. Now you can have fun playing a raunchy fantasy where she is at your mercy from loads of luscious teasing! You can take some lubricant and a feather and tickle around her clitoris. You can run it up and down her labia. If she's game for more restraint, you can put some soft, fur-lined handcuffs on her wrists so that she really can't stop you teasing her intimately. Of course, fair's fair, so he should have a turn at having his ankles tied apart and being pleasured in whatever way she wants to pleasure him.

Sensual Self-Pleasure

All of us wonder about how our partners masturbate. We are endlessly curious and many people have confided to me that they'd love to know what their partner gets up to. In fact, they say they'd be very turned on if allowed to watch. More often than not a man agrees to stimulate himself with his hand while his partner watches. But what's really sexy is to build up the confidence to masturbate together.

There are a couple of tricks to making this successful and the first one is to turn it into 'something else'. If you ask someone directly (even your lover) if they'll masturbate while you do, it can be a bit daunting. Instead turn into a little bit of a game of, 'I'll show you, if you show me'. While you're enjoying a little foreplay you can say something like, 'Let me show you how I touch my clitoris. Then I'd like to know how you stroke your penis (or whatever nickname you use).' And then you can both take it from there.

Also, a couple of other tips to help this along include making sure you use subtle lighting so that the mood feels really sensual. Next, make sure you choose the time wisely and suggest such sex-play when you're both feeling relaxed. You can also encourage the more sexually confident one of you to take the lead. Either they can take the lead as I suggest above, or they can simply lie back and start to show the other what they do to themselves when on their own.

Slowly Does It

Now that you've familiarised yourself with butt plugs it's time to try a little technique with anal beads. As with butt plugs, these can be bought in various sizes and are strung together four or five at a time. People often put them in before sex-play to heighten their pleasure as when they move around, the beads move around inside them.

But here's a fantastic way to make your orgasms more powerful. Insert the anal beads as the instructions say. They will have a safety string with which to remove them. Ask your partner to pull on the string slowly, sliding the beads out one at a time as you reach orgasm. Your orgasm will feel amazing! The next time you use the anal beads you can return the favour when they orgasm. Or, if you have recovered from your orgasm, then when your partner reaches theirs you can do it to them slowly and sensually. One or both of you may lose concentration around the point of your climax if you try to do this simultaneously.

Kinky Knickers

Some kinky knickers, like the crutchless ones, do have a point! You may think they sound awful and tacky but this tip can provide you with a hot evening out. Slip some crutchless knickers on before you go out. Then, when you're sitting together sharing a drink, or looking at the menu in a restaurant, you can guide his hand up your skirt to your saucy surprise. He can fondle you to your heart's content with the easy access the crutchless knickers provide. Also, if things get really steamy you can find somewhere to have a quickie and these will give him easy access for penetrative sex. So, never turn your nose up at a pair of these because they may give you one really raunchy evening out!

Buttock Bonk

Sometimes we do things for our lover that maybe doesn't give us a lot of pleasure. As long as it's not a turn-off – or done under pressure – it can be a great thing to please your partner in a way that turns them on. This goes both ways between partners and you should expect the favour back!

An interesting trick that's a twist on this is for you to allow him to indulge in a 'buttock bonk'. This is not full anal sex (that's coming below). Instead, it's where he thrusts gently between the cleft of your buttocks, but does not enter you. If he's a bit of a bum-man he'll love this. He can slip and slide with lots of lubricant. Obviously as he passes back and forth between your cheeks he should wear a condom so as not to pick up any bacteria; even if you're freshly showered this is still a risk.

Pearl Necklaces

Men like to try all sorts of dirty delights! I suppose you could say a pearl necklace is one of these. Some women get off on having their partner ejaculate over them. Others will hate it and shouldn't feel the pressure to allow it. The Pearl Necklace gets its name from the fact that usually after a man's been thrusting between his partner's breasts (a Breast Bonk) he then ejaculates over her cleavage and neck. Of course, his ejaculate looks like little pearls!

Go for it unless it disgusts either of you. But a little tip to keep things tidy is to always have a box of tissues next to the bedside table so that she can wipe his ejaculate off. A fantastic trick for her is to gently cup his testicles as he kneels across/above/beside her and to gently pull them in a rhythmical fashion as he approaches his climax. He should tell her when he's getting near to climax so she can start this extra stimulation. He'll have such a great orgasm that she can expect some sort of pleasure in return!

Special Spanking

This technique is for the 'naughty' man or woman. Anyone who likes a little bit of anal-play as well as spanking will love this technique. The partner to be spanked lies across their partner's lap. The spanker uses one hand to spank his partner's bottom while he slowly slides his finger into their bottom, as always, using loads of lubrication and wearing some sort of barrier on his finger, like a condom or latex glove.

To add a little finesse, the spanker can rhythmically insert their finger in and out – just an inch or so – as they spank. By doing this in synchrony they can build an intense sexual desire in their partner. An extra little tip to add to this is to use some fantasy chat of the sub-dom-relationship type. Perhaps you can pretend you're a dominatrix spanking his bottom. Or he pretends he's the college lecturer and he's punishing you for getting your thesis in late. Anything goes!

Captive Clitoris

Now we can get into a little bit of bondage-play with this trick. This can be fantastic for the woman who has learnt to let go of her inhibitions and is experimenting with how far she can go in playing the role of 'exhibitionist'. This takes a fun, sex-perimental attitude on both partners' sides. It's a great little trick for building her sexual desire. She should be handcuffed (with some comfortable handcuffs!) and her legs spread and each ankle tied so that she's spread-eagled on the bed. After gently and tenderly massaging her pelvis, hips, inner thighs and pubic mound with some lovely lubricant, he gently pulls up her clitoral hood. Now, he gently blows across her clitoris. Then he can gently circle it – but not touch it – with the tip of his tongue. With a little finesse and care he'll drive her absolutely crazy!

Share Her Juices!

As with many of these techniques they should only be used with partners who know each other's sexual histories and can share bodily fluids. This is one to do when you give her oral pleasure. It's hot and sexy and you'll seem like a very sophisticated lover. When you go down on her, carefully suck some of her juices into your mouth. Then come up to her mouth and kiss her carefully as you dribble some droplets of her juices into her mouth.

Linger there, kissing each other and savouring her taste. You can, of course, go down on her as many times as you want and come back to kiss her.

Anal Sex Tip No.1

Some people love anal sex, some people hate it, and some people don't really know where to start. Where some couples enjoy a little experimentation, other couples may like regular anal sex. People vary tremendously but what's important is to take the fear out of it, if you want to try it. The very first and important thing to remember (aside from safe-sex practices), is gently does it. A man shouldn't try and force his erect penis into his partner's anus and a woman shouldn't try and force a vibrator into a man's anus.

The best way to start is one finger at a time! Imagine that you've been enjoying foreplay, kissing and caressing each other all over your bodies. You know you're both up for a little anal-pleasure so you slip that condom on to your finger, apply some condom-friendly lubricant, and gently tickle the rim of your partner's anus. This goes for both men and women. As they relax – and ask them how they're feeling, whether relaxed or a little tense – slowly nudge it up. Keep checking they feel comfortable and you can progress to a gentle in-and-out motion with your fingertip.

Anal Sex Tip No.2

This is a great trick that you should definitely use if you're going to be penetrated anally. What you need to do is expel any trapped wind and the best way to do this is to go into the privacy of your bathroom. Get down on all fours and tip your hips into the air – gas rises! Now, try to expel any as you stay in that position for a couple of minutes. This way, when your partner begins to penetrate you either with their finger, sex toy or penis, you're less likely to make embarrassing noises. Also, if there's any chance you need to empty your bowels then do so, wash thoroughly and then you can relax.

Anal Sex Tip No.3

Whether a woman's going to be penetrated by his penis, or a man's going to be penetrated by a strap-on or vibrator, you need to take it easy. The key trick here is that if you're going to be penetrated you need to relax your anal sphincter as you're being penetrated. This makes penetration easier. You can do this by imitating the action as if you're trying to pass wind – this relaxes the sphincter momentarily making penetration easier. Remember, for both of your enjoyment, partial penetration may be all that's achieved.

It Hurts So Good

Many people experiment with a little bit of S&M – sado-masochistic sex-play. The combination of pain and pleasure in sexual arousal has been around for centuries. Most people associate this with a little spanking and whipping for heightening their pleasure. The most important tip to remember if you are spanking or whipping your partner is to make sure you move across the areas of skin being struck. If you repeatedly whip or spank the same spot (and if you enjoy this type of sex-play regularly), you can damage the tissue. So, imagine that you're whipping your partner's buttock – slowly inch across the area as you actually strike it. Then you can move across their buttock backwards, to where you began striking.

You can be creative with what you use. You don't have to purchase an expensive leather whip, crop or strap – a big, wooden spoon from the kitchen or the back of a hairbrush works fine for some sex-perimentation. If you both find that you enjoy it then there are all sorts of things you can buy from adult shops.

You might start with some smacking or whipping but as you get into full-body contact you'll have to put down your whip or your hairbrush (or whatever you've been using). Then, simple pinching and slapping with your hand will keep the heightened sensations alive as you come to orgasm.

Dress It Up

A fantastic thing about a little bit of S&M or sub-dom sex-play is that there is a huge array of clothing that goes along with it. There's lots of fetish gear to choose from and everyone's taste can be catered for. A wise tip is not to wear fetish gear from top to toe. That can look ridiculous – if you've ever been to a fetish party you'll know the sort of look that I'm talking about. Instead, select carefully and you'll make a bigger impact on your lover. Choose some fetish boots and a corset top but pair them with a plain mini-skirt. For the man, he might want to wear a fetish-style leather waistcoat while he wields the whip but skip the fetish trousers that go with it.

Once you're dressed for sex-cess you'll also find role play comes a lot easier. I find this works fantastically with people that have been a bit inhibited. If they slip into some S&M gear they find they can really let go. It's very releasing and I think all couples should experiment with at least something like a little bit of 'vanilla' bondage.

Unless you are new lovers, you should know your partner well enough to realise what sort of language is acceptable to them when you're enjoying this sort of sex-play. You can let loose with a load of filth or moderate it depending on your partner's tastes.

Sexy and Safe, Care and Caution

Many people who enjoy S&M sex-play get carried away and end up in A&E rooms in hospitals across the country. So it's important I give you a couple of crucial tips to think about when you're doing anything that involves pleasure and pain. For example, never whip anywhere near your partner's face – you don't want to take their eye out! Also, never whip your partner's genitals as a laceration can lead to serious damage. Drinking and recreational drugs can also dull your pain threshold, so you should be sober (or only mildly tipsy, having had a maximum of one or two drinks) so that your pain threshold is still intact and you don't take things too far.

Another tip is the use of codewords for safe sex-play. This is important because if you're in a role play and say something like, 'Don't, stop, I don't want to do this anymore', it could be misinterpreted as part of your 'character'. For example, if you're playing a 'virgin maid' in a Victorian household trapped by a handsome visitor and are being 'toyed with', your character may say that to increase excitement for you both. So, always designate a codeword, or safe word, that is neutral and won't be confused with part of the role play.

U-Spot Stimulation

Just as some women swear by G-spot stimulation, other women swear by a little place called the U-spot. The U-spot is a small area of delicate skin that's located above the opening of the urethral canal, roughly about half a centimetre below the clitoris. The urethral opening is located just above the opening to the vagina. Some women love having this U-spot area lightly touched or rubbed with the finger, tongue or even the nose. Some liken it to rubbing the magic genie of sexual excitement! Sex researchers have said that pressure might be built up through the gentle rubbing – and that it might lead to secretions building up inside the glans of the vagina.

Why not turn this into a 'sex doctor and patient' fantasy role play? The sex doctor has to explore her U-spot region and try to get her excited by trying different types of touch.

Sextion Four

The 'Deluxe Dozen' Selection

Here are a Deluxe Dozen tips, tricks and techniques for enhancing your pleasure. I call them 'deluxe' because whether they're simple or sophisticated, or just plain fun, they're sexy and really will enhance your sex life.

'V' is for Victory

This is a favourite technique, as not only is it extremly simple but also I've never come across a woman that didn't get incredibly aroused by it. Even for a woman who has difficulty getting aroused, it can work wonders. It's a real teasing sensation that the man can do for as long as she desires.

Imagine that the man uses his index and middle fingers to form a classic V-sign. However, he doesn't close his thumb and outer two fingers into his palm. They simply relax outwards away from the V-sign. Now he slips the V-sign over her pubic mound, moving his two fingertips downwards (towards her perineum/bottom) so that his index finger covers one of her labia and his middle finger covers her other labia. He only slips them down over her labia to roughly the point that her clitoris ends up in line with his finger joints nearest to the palm of his hand. The placement is important so that as he moves his V-sign lightly forwards and backwards skimming her labia, her clitoris is not really touched by the palm of his hand at the base of his fingers. In this way, her clitoris never gets fully stimulated but instead her clitoral region generally is stimulated, getting maximum teasing that arouses her clitoris.

He can keep this gentle rocking-action going as long as she can take it – many women are soon begging to have full sex because it's such a teasing sensation.

Ripe as a Peach

This is a lovely and sensual little trick he can use when giving her oral pleasure. Taking a ripe peach that he's split in half, he gently squeezes some of the juice over her labia. First, taking his fingers, with his index and middle finger together, he can slide the droplets of juice around and around her labia. Then he can go down to kiss and lick her before squeezing a little more juice on to her labia. Of course, he can substitute his favourite fruit for the peach or use any fruit that they have to hand that's juicy, like ripe melon, mango or papaya.

Honey 'Lips'

Here's a super sweet and sexy oral sex technique she can do to tantalise him. She needs a pot of honey by the bedside. He's lying flat on his back and she straddles him so that he can lap at her labia and vagina. She dips her fingers into the honey and spreads just a little bit on to her labia. The warmth of her skin warms the honey so that it oozes on to his lips as he gives her oral pleasure. She can straddle him for as long as she likes and dip into the honeypot as frequently as she likes while he licks at her 'honeypot'!

SIZZLING SEX

The Sexy Snake

He can use this sexy little finger technique to really stimulate the inside of her vagina. When he is manually arousing her vagina, using this trick will get her turned on quickly and become highly lubricated. After some general stroking and touching of her outer vagina he puts his index and middle fingers together, slowly slips them up inside, then gently wiggles them around like a snake – imagine the 'squiggle' movement that a snake makes when it slithers. This movement ensures that he touches all the inside walls of her vagina. As the pressure from his fingers touch one wall, the other walls of her vagina long to be retouched.

Silky Scarf and Panty Play

If women find it hard to get aroused or reach orgasm, one of the best tricks to use is another one that produces a teasing sensation. The more a non-orgasmic woman is teased, the more likely it is that she'll get fully aroused – and end up getting pleased! Use any silky scarf that you don't mind getting covered with her natural lubrication. Or use any of her silky panties. Having stripped her silky panties off carefully and sensuously, take them between your hand and lightly run their silkiness down her pubic mound, her labia, around her perineum and back up again. Repeat the cycle many times and very gently.

You can do the same manoeuvre with her silky scarf. But with her scarf use this hot little tip – gently slip her on to her side, facing you, and slip the silky scarf between her legs. Now reach one hand around behind her to grab one end of the scarf as the other hand grabs the end in front of her. Now move your hands up and down and back and forth to glide across her labia. Simply stunning pleasure!

The Whole Body Orgasm

Every couple should try this technique at least once. Even if ultimately you feel it doesn't benefit both of you, it can help teach you about your sexual responses. And knowledge is good!

In this technique you do some opposite things to what you normally do with your body during sex. As your kissing and caressing builds, and you're beginning to think about full sex, the first thing I'd like you to do is to listen for each other's breathing and start breathing together. Right now you're not yet having full sex, but simply try synchronising your general bodily movements (as you hold each other and touch each other) together.

As you feel your breathing is becoming in time with each other, then you should start full sex. Once you're having penetrative sex you can begin to start to relax your muscles. What we normally do is tense our muscles as we get nearer to climax. You can softly whisper to each other at this point, reminding each other to relax your muscles.

Now you can think about your breathing again and do the opposite of what you normally do during full sex: normally your breathing would get more shallow and quicker as you get more excited, but I want you to try to slow it down. Once you're relaxing your muscles and slowing your breathing, try to clear your mind – letting go of any thoughts. Try to think of nothing except relaxing your muscles, slowing your breathing and listening to your lover.

Couples who manage to learn this technique say they have immensely powerful orgasms throughout the whole body. This may be because during a 'normal' orgasm we're all tensed up and so the focus of the orgasm is narrowed. However, if you are letting your muscles relax, your breathing slow, and your mind remains clear, the orgasm can ripple through your whole body.

Vibe for Two

This is a gorgeous twist on classic 69-style sex. Get yourselves into the side-by-side, facing each other, 69 position and have your two favourite vibrators to hand – the one he likes to be teased with most and the one she likes to be teased with most. Each of you will do the following: part your lover's thighs and begin by stroking back and forth across their pubic bone with their favourite vibrator and with your free hand placed flat on their perineum, simply holding that area. After you've stimulated their pubic region then stroke the vibrator around his testicles, down his perineum and back up again. And for her, stroke the vibrator down her labia, down her perineum, and back up again. Don't make a big deal of it but try to get your strokes in rhythm with each other as you go up and down and around with your vibrators. You'd be surprised but you'll find you probably get into a rhythm with each other and end up stroking each other at the same time.

Al Fresco Sex

I don't want you to get into trouble with the law about out-of-doors sex, however, every couple should enjoy some sort of outdoor naughtiness. There's something about doing a sex act when you might get caught that makes it terribly exciting. The best tip is to always have something to hand that you can throw over yourselves to cover up if someone comes past. For example, if you're on holiday and you decide to have sex on a reclining beach chair at your hotel one starlit night, then bring along a big beach towel to throw over yourselves if need be. You can smile innocently if someone strolls past, pretending you're just cuddling up together under the towel.

The other big no-no is thinking you can get your partner to have sex, say, out in a forest or field and not thinking about their comfort. Always have a picnic blanket or at least a thick jacket to put under them for their comfort. Another trick is to pleasure each other with your hands or through oral sex when out of doors. One of you can keep a watch for anyone approaching. It heightens your anticipation and sense of risk. Just simply starting your foreplay when out and about but saving finishing each other off until you both get home can lead to exhilarating sex.

The Cascade

A fantastic technique to do for each other is the Cascade. One of you is lying back and the other one pleasures them in this way: drizzle lots of luscious lubricant down their breasts/chest, stomach and hips. Take a vibrator – or two, one in each hand – and beginning at their collarbone, gently swirl them back and forth through the lubricant all the way down to their hips. Try to get a real cascading motion going so they feel a cascade of arousal and stimulation from top to bottom as you move down their body. Re-apply the lubricant as often as necessary. You can then swap places so the other can have this sensual experience. Ideally invest in a couple of fingertip vibrators – one for each hand – for the perfect cascading sensation.

Flashlight Fantasy

Here's a naughty little game to try – guaranteed to give you some fun and hopefully a sexy romp! I include this in my Deluxe Dozen because it involves a basic household implement that anyone can get hold of (a torch), fun, raunchiness (peeking into dark corners under sheets), a little fantasy play (being 'explorers'), as well as lots of intimate touching and licking. All these are good basic things that when pulled together into a little technique will prove that you can kick-start some really fun sex with the simplest of techniques. Get a torch and agree that you'll take turns exploring with it. The Explorer gets to dive under the sheets for a lingering look at their lover's body – their flashlight fantasy. Wherever he/she points the light they have to stroke that area and plant a long and lingering kiss on that erogenous zone. You then swap over and allow the other person to have a turn exploring between the sheets with their flashlight fantasy.

The Ultimate Tease

Building sexual tension between you in the easiest possible way is one of the best, sure-fire ways to give you more powerful orgasms. Both of you can try this tip but in slightly different ways.

To tease him: when you've been indulging in lots of kissing, caressing and foreplay then sit astride him and gently glide your well-lubricated labia up and down his erect penis until he can't take it anymore and needs to enter you. If you take your time, not only do you build up your desire but definitely his! You can alternate the sensation you give him by sitting astride him but using very small pelvic thrusts to gently bump your labia against his shaft.

To tease her: when you're both really excited have her lie back and open her legs. Take your erect penis firmly in your hand and slip your glans up and down her labia without entering her. As you get more skilled, or get a good rhythm going, you can move it up her labia, nudge or lightly circle her clitoris, before moving back down her labia. Repeat this movement as many times as you can stand it without starting full sex.

Strip Tease and Please

There's one thing that I repeatedly get told in confidence that a person would like their lover to do – and that's strip off for them! Not only men ask for this but women do too. There is something about knowing that the trust between you has built up to the point where you'll do a little bit of a sexy strip to please your partner. Here are the best tips to make sure you feel confident doing this (and I'm talking to the men here too!).

First, you have to choose something to strip out of that you feel sexy and confident in. It shouldn't have any tricky buckles or buttons that are fiddly. It's never sexy when you have to struggle out of something during a strip! Next you need to choose music that you feel sexy moving to – it may be some moody R'n'B or heavy rock – it's your choice. Now practice makes perfect. Check yourself out in a mirror while you're moving. Decide what looks good and makes you feel sexy. Linger over moves that involve pulsating your hips. Practise moves where you gently stroke your fingertips right over your body. Once you're wearing something sexy and have practised to the music, then it's time to sort out the lighting in your sitting room or bedroom. Now you're ready to go!

For an extra naughty little trick, you can agree to do the strip for your partner as long as they're tied to the bed. You can then caress and stroke them in between your moves – a fantastic way to get them desperate for full sex.

There you go – those are the 250 top sex tips, tricks and techniques to set your sex life on fire. These should give you hours and hours of sexy fun and stimulate you to try your own fresh ideas.

Enjoy!

Dr Pam x

Websites

Here is a selection of the many adult websites out there. Most of these are straightforward sites selling a range of sex toys and products, though I have added notes for those that offer information, advice or other services. **It is your responsibility to ensure that at the time of use any website is secure.**

Please note that all these websites are prefixed with www.

adameve.com

agentprovocateur.com

amandakiss.co.uk

angelicweapons.co.uk

annsummers.com

athenafem.co.uk – for pelvic muscle exercisers

bedroompleasures.co.uk

blissbox.com

blushingbuyer.co.uk

cherrybliss.com

cliterati.co.uk

coco-de-mer.co.uk

condomania.co.uk

couplebox.com – software to store your private pictures securely

curiosa.co.uk – for erotica

doublydiscreet.com

dreamgirldirect.co.uk

elegantlywaisted.co.uk

emotionalbliss.com

erotica-readers.co.uk

eroticprints.org

eternalspirits.com

femininezone.com – for information and advice

femmefun.com

fetteredpleasures.com

flirtyordirty.co.uk

getmepleasure.co.uk

glamorousamorous.com

goodvibes.com

highestheaven.co.uk

hunkystrippers.com

idlube.co.uk – specialises in lubricants

lovehoney.co.uk

male101.com – about male sexuality

mencorp.com – for strippers

menforalloccasions.com – for escorts

mr-s-leather-fetters.com

myla.com

natural-contours.com

no-angel.com

passion8.com – erotica

pelvictoner.co.uk

pillowtalk.co.uk

scarletmagazine.co.uk – a sexy monthly magazine for women

sda.uk.net – the Sexual Dysfunction Association

serpentstail.com – for hot reading

sexchampionships.com – a sex game to play online

sexplained.com – for information on STIs, etc

sexshop365.co.uk

sextoys.co.uk

sh-womenstore.com

shesaidboutique.com

skintwo.com

slapdat.co.uk – a butt-slapping fun site

slashfic.co.uk – your favourite fictional characters are given hot scenes

takemetobed.co.uk – for erotica and porn

thesexystore.co.uk

whysleep.co.uk

wickedlywildwomen.com

willyworries.com